Laboratory Manual to Accompany Chemistry 110

Community College of Philadelphia

CENGAGE
Learning™

Australia • Brazil • Japan • Korea • Mexico • Singapore • Spain • United Kingdom • United States

CENGAGE
Learning™

Laboratory Manual to Accompany Chemistry 110

Chemical Principles in the Laboratory, 8th Edition
Emil Slowinski | Wayne C. Wolsey | William L. Masterton

© 2005 Cengage Learning. All rights reserved.

Introduction to Chemical Principles: A Laboratory Approach, 6th Edition
Susan A. Weiner

© 2005 Cengage Learning. All rights reserved.

Executive Editors:
Maureen Staudt
Michael Stranz

World of Chemistry, Lab Manual (Extended Version)
Joesten

© 1996 Cengage Learning. All rights reserved.

Senior Project Development Manager:
Linda deStefano

Marketing Specialist:
Courtney Sheldon

Senior Production/Manufacturing Manager:
Donna M. Brown

Original work provided for Experiments 5, 10, and 17
Kathleen Harter | William Eisen | Michael Byler | Robert Melucci

PreMedia Manager:
Joel Brennecke

Sr. Rights Acquisition Account Manager:
Todd Osborne

Cover Image:
stock.xchng

For product information and technology assistance, contact us at
Cengage Learning Customer & Sales Support, 1-800-354-9706

For permission to use material from this text or product,
submit all requests online at **cengage.com/permissions**
Further permissions questions can be emailed to
permissionrequest@cengage.com

This book contains select works from existing Cengage Learning resources and was produced by Cengage Learning Custom Solutions for collegiate use. As such, those adopting and/or contributing to this work are responsible for editorial content accuracy, continuity and completeness.

Compilation © 2011 Cengage Learning
ISBN-13: 978-1-133-44776-4

ISBN-10: 1-133-44776-7

Cengage Learning
5191 Natorp Boulevard
Mason, Ohio 45040
USA
Cengage Learning is a leading provider of customized learning solutions with office locations around the globe, including Singapore, the United Kingdom, Australia, Mexico, Brazil, and Japan. Locate your local office at:
international.cengage.com/region.

Cengage Learning products are represented in Canada by Nelson Education, Ltd.
For your lifelong learning solutions, visit **www.cengage.com/custom.**
Visit our corporate website at **www.cengage.com.**

Printed in the United States of America

Table of Contents

DEPARTMENT OF CHEMISTRY
COMMUNITY COLLEGE OF PHILADELPHIA

LABORATORY CHECK-IN PROCEDURES

INSTRUCTIONS

Please read all the material carefully and adhere to the guidelines and safety rules in this package. After reading the Department Information and Laboratory Rules, hearing the safety lecture and checking in your drawer, etc., please sign the *Certification Statement* and return it to your Laboratory Instructor. You will not be permitted to do laboratory work unless you have signed and returned the statement.

CONTENTS:

A. Department Information

B. Departmental Laboratory Policy

C. Experiment Report Sheet (Sample)

D. Laboratory Rules

E. Equipment Procedures
    a. I General
    b. II Fire Extinguisher Use

F. Schematic

G. Demonstration and Practice in using a Bunsen Burner

H. Apparatus Lists

I. Safety Test (Lecture Copy)

J. Certification Statement

A: DEPARMENT INFORMATION

Students are not permitted in the laboratory without an instructor present.

Only the assigned experiment may be performed.

There will be **no laboratory experiment make-ups.** Experiments will only run on the assigned day. It is your responsibility to attend the assigned laboratory period.

No visitors are allowed in the laboratory unless approved by the instructor.
If approval is given, visitors must wear safety goggles.

Children are not permitted in the laboratory at any time.

Please do not bring valuables in to the laboratory. We are not responsible for lost or stolen valuables, so it is best to leave them in your locker or at home.

It is usually advisable to make use of an "experiment report sheet" when handing in experiments or laboratory reports (see B: sample *Experiment Report Sheet*).

IF NEEDED
The **Nurse's** office is located in the Mint Building – Room M1-21, extension 8181 and 8182.
[Availability 9 to 5 Monday through Friday]
The **Security** Office is Located at M1-23, extension 8111.
- **The college security main office has an emergency number 5555. This is only to be used in a critical life and death situation.**

NOTE
Any collected laboratory **notebooks will be discarded** if not picked up directly from your instructor or from room W4-50 no later than two weeks into the next semester.

READ
Department memo of December 2004 (following pages) for important information regarding lab grading

CHEMISTRY DEPARTMENT
M E M O R A N D U M

TO: **All CCP Chemistry Students**
FROM: Department of Chemistry Laboratory Committee
DATE: December 8, 2004
SUBJECT: Laboratory Policy

Chemistry is a laboratory science and laboratory work is an integral part of the chemistry course. Attendance is critical! Satisfactory completion of the laboratory portion of the course will account for 20% of your course grade.

A satisfactory grade in both the lecture AND laboratory are required to pass the course. Failure of either of these will result in failure of the chemistry course.

It is NOT possible to withdraw **only** from lecture **or** from lab.
Likewise, if repeating a course, both lecture and lab **must** be part of your registered class schedule.

Laboratory Requirements:
1. The Laboratory Safety Test.
2. Laboratory Experiments.
3. Laboratory Notebook.
4. Laboratory Reports
5. Laboratory Quizzes.
6. Work performance in the laboratory.

1.   **The Safety Test.**
    The safety test is given at the beginning of the semester and addresses many aspects of laboratory safety. **You must get a grade of 100%** in order to be permitted to work in the laboratory. Your safety test will be kept on file by your instructor.

2.   **Laboratory Experiments.**
    Students are required to attend **every** laboratory session and to perform **all** scheduled experiments.
    There are no make-ups permitted by attending other sections.
    If you miss a lab, it is imperative that you **consult your laboratory instructor immediately** either in person, by telephone or by e-mail.
    A student who misses **3** laboratories over the course of the semester (for any and all reasons, excused or unexcused, including lateness) will **fail** the laboratory portion of the course and therefore the entire course.

3. **Laboratory Notebook.**

Keeping of a laboratory **notebook is required**. A satisfactory laboratory notebook, prepared in accordance with directions provided by your instructor, must be completed and used in lab during every lab session.

It is highly likely that your purchased *lab manual* will NOT be allowed in the lab.

4. **Laboratory Reports.**

Laboratory reports for each experiment, prepared in accordance with directions provided by your instructor, must be completed and turned in on time.

5. **Laboratory Quizzes.**

Quizzes are given at the discretion of your instructor. A passing average in laboratory quizzes must be attained.

6. **Work Performance.**

Performance is evaluated on preparedness for laboratory, understanding of the experiment, improvement in technical competence as the semester progresses, and adherence to safety rules.

Your instructor will determine his/her exact criteria for evaluating these competencies.

Your Laboratory Grade is based on the following factors:
   a. Laboratory Notebook
   b. Laboratory Reports
   c. Laboratory Quizzes
   d. Work Performance

Lateness to Lab

You are expected to be in the laboratory on time. Each lab class begins with a pre-lab lecture which explains the procedure and safety precautions for the scheduled experiment. If you are late for lab, you are a safety hazard to other students and yourself. For that reason, **NO STUDENTS WILL BE ADMITTED TO THE LAB LATE** and you may not perform the scheduled experiment. *Remember: a missed lab, for any reason, counts as an absence.*

ChemLabPolicy HarterSharedFile
9/17/04

C: *SAMPLE* EXPERIMENT REPORT SHEET
(A supply of these sheets may be found stored in the lab)

COMMUNITY COLLEGE OF PHILADELPHIA
DEPARTMENT OF CHEMISTRY

EXPERIMENT REPORT SHEET

NAME_____ DATE_____

PARTNER(S)_____

LABORATORY INSTRUCTOR_____

COURSE NUMBER_____   SECTION NUMBER_____

LABORATORY MANUAL _____

EXPERIMENT TITLE & NUMBER_____

_____

UNKNOWN NUMBER_____

D: LABORATORY RULES

1. **Pennsylvania State Law: Safety goggles or approved eye protection must be worn at all times in the laboratory.** Failure to comply will result in dismissal from the laboratory. Wear eyeglasses while working in the laboratory at all times. Contact lenses are **not** eye protection and are highly discouraged because they may trap chemicals in the eye!
   Stated in the Journal of Chemical Education: Volume 63, November 11, 1989, "Out of 55 accidents, a total of 80% were to the head/eye/face area: 68% alone were to the eyes."

2. Protect open cuts by keeping them covered.

3. No foodstuffs or drinks of any kind (including gum) and no electronic devices of any type (including cell phones) are allowed in the laboratory.

4. Confine all loose clothing, (i.e. neckties, scarves, etc) and hair in the laboratory. Only wear close-toed, low-heeled shoes. Note: tank tops and sandals are strictly prohibited.

5. Each student is responsible for keeping his/her drawer and work area clean. The entire class is responsible for keeping the laboratory clean.

6. Do not force glass tubing into rubber stoppers. Make sure the glass is fire-polished and lubricated with glycerin. Protect your hands with a thick pad of paper towels. Your instructor will demonstrate.

7. Do not arbitrarily mix chemicals!! Know what you are doing!

8. Never taste any chemicals. Never pipet solutions my mouth; always use a pipet filler or bulb.

9. Exercise great care in noting the odor of fumes **and** avoid direct breathing of any kind. Use the fume hood for dangerous or irritating chemicals.

10. When working with organic chemicals, do not use rubber stoppers. Organic chemicals **must** be stoppered with corks.

11. Clean up spilled materials immediately and dispose of them properly. Do not dispose of solid materials in the sink.

12. Do not store any chemicals in your drawer. They may be volatile or flammable and could cause injury to others.

13. Do not place any piece of apparatus or chemicals directly into the Bunsen burner flame.

14. Never heat volatile or flammable materials with a Bunsen burner unless instructed to do so and how to do it by your instructor.

15. Follow the safety policies and your instructor's directions concerning the disposal of waste materials, chemicals, and broken glass.

16. Since each apparatus set-up differs slightly, you must have your instructor's approval before you begin to work to ensure maximum safety. **Photographs** of the most common basic lab set-ups can be found on the front bulletin board in each lab.

17. Do not use instruments unless assigned to do so and then only after the instructor has demonstrated how to operate the instrument.

18. Use only those balances (for weighing) that your instructor designates for your class.
    - Do not place hot items on the balance pans.
    - Do not weigh material directly on the balance pan—use weighing paper or other containers.
    - Clean up all spilled chemicals
    - Always return the balance to zero or its rest point when finished.

19. Report all accidents **IMMEDIATELY** to your instructor.

20. **Wash your hands before leaving the laboratory. Make this a habit!**

E I: EQUIPMENT PROCEDURES (General):

1. Compare the contents of your equipment drawer and the appropriate *Apparatus List* for your course. The apparatus list does contain some diagrams to help you identify the equipment.

2. If an item in your drawer is not on the Apparatus List, remove it and place it on the front bench. Equipment drawers should contain only those items on your list.

3. If an item on your Apparatus List is not in your drawer, notify your instructor and it will be replaced.

4. If you discover glassware that is chipped, cracked, or broken, please discard it in the proper manner (*broken glass only* container) and replace it with undamaged pieces.

5. Accessory equipment is utilized repeatedly during laboratory periods. This equipment is not stored in your drawer. This equipment is stored throughout the laboratory and **must** be returned to its proper container or storage area at the end of the period..

6. If additional equipment or special apparatus is issued to you during the laboratory period, it must be returned to the instructor after the laboratory period is over.

7. During your last laboratory period, you will clean and check out your equipment drawer. This includes removing the contents, cleaning the drawer/locker, cleaning the equipment, and replacing any missing or damaged equipment. Check-out is mandatory. **A student will not receive a grade until check-out is completed.**

8. If a student withdraws prior to the end of the semester, check-out must still be accomplished. **The college will hold all grades until check-out is completed.**

E II: EXTINGUISHING FIRES:

Listed below is a logical and simple pattern of steps that can be employed when using a fire extinguisher.

1. Take the fire extinguisher off of the wall.

2. Break the plastic seal holding the pin in place.

3. Pull the pin out.

4. Stand back away from the fire -6 to 8 feet.

5. Aim the extinguisher nozzle at the base of the fire.

6. Squeeze the handle the discharge the fire extinguisher.

7. While the extinguisher is discharging move it from side to side moderately to cover the entire base of the fire.

F: LABORATORY SCHEMATIC:

On the next page is a schematic of the laboratory on which you should note the location of these important pieces of emergency and safety equipment. **Your instructor will point them out to you and show you how to operate them.** It is extremely important that you learn the location of all laboratory emergency cut off switches and safety equipment in order to be prepared in case an emergency should occur.

A. Gas Cut Off

B. Water Cut Offs (Hot and Cold)

C. Air Cut Off

D. Steam Cut Off (Room W4-47 only)

E. Ventilation Hood Control Boxes (6)

F. Fire Extinguishers (5)

G. Emergency Lighting

H. Safety Shower

I. Fire Blanket

J. Eye Wash Station

In addition, you will note that the schematic shows the location of the commonly used items which are not stored in your drawer. **Your instructor will also point out these locations to you. He/she will demonstrate how to use these pieces of specialized equipment (ex. crucibles, burets, etc.) when needed.**

G: Demonstration and Practice in using a Bunsen Burner

Please pay close attention to your instructor in order to learn to safely use this vital piece of laboratory equipment. **Exercise care when you first ignite your burner.**

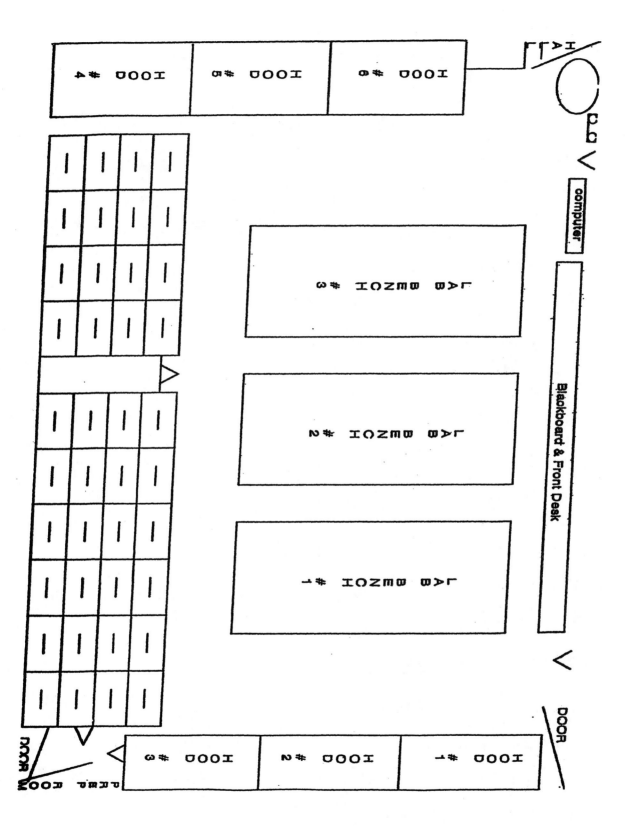

H: Apparatus Lists

APPARATUS LIST FOR 101, 102, 105, 110, 118, 121, 122

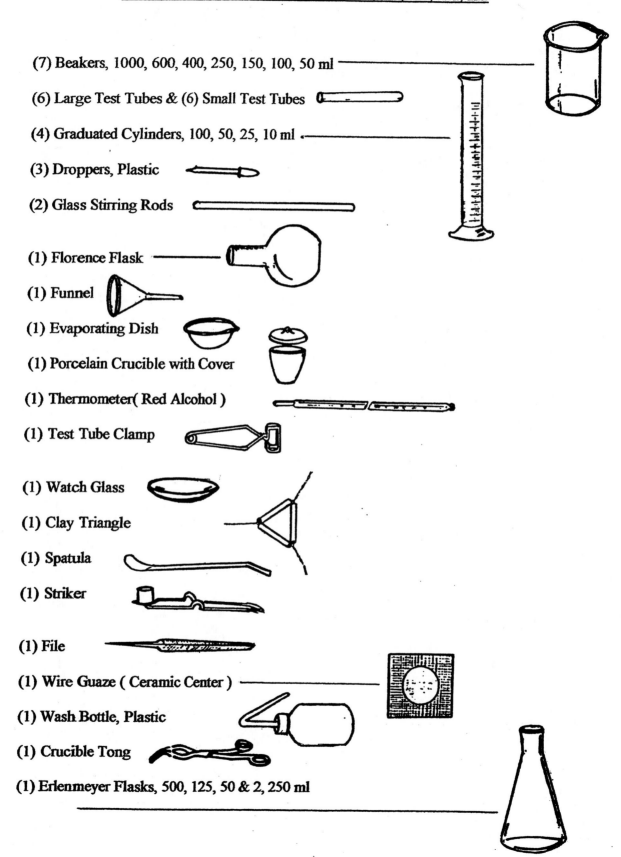

(7) Beakers, 1000, 600, 400, 250, 150, 100, 50 ml

(6) Large Test Tubes & (6) Small Test Tubes

(4) Graduated Cylinders, 100, 50, 25, 10 ml

(3) Droppers, Plastic

(2) Glass Stirring Rods

(1) Florence Flask

(1) Funnel

(1) Evaporating Dish

(1) Porcelain Crucible with Cover

(1) Thermometer(Red Alcohol)

(1) Test Tube Clamp

(1) Watch Glass

(1) Clay Triangle

(1) Spatula

(1) Striker

(1) File

(1) Wire Guaze (Ceramic Center)

(1) Wash Bottle, Plastic

(1) Crucible Tong

(1) Erlenmeyer Flasks, 500, 125, 50 & 2, 250 ml

I: Safety Procedures Test - Lecture Copy

1. Who should be immediately called for assistance in case of an accident or injury in the laboratory?_____

2. What must be worn in a laboratory at all times to decrease the likelihood of an eye injury?_____

3. a) What should you do if something gets in your eye?_____

   _____

   b) What device can you use to help? Note their location._____

   _____

4. a) What should be immediately used for a large chemical spill on your clothing?

   _____

   b) Where is it?_____

5. Why is it important to keep the laboratory benches free of book bags, coats, etc.?

   _____

6. Why is it forbidden to wear headphones in the laboratory?_____

   _____

7. What precautions have to be taken with equipment that was *or* is being heated (e.g. crucibles, ringstands, etc.)? _____

   _____

8. Why is it dangerous to leave an ignited Bunsen burner unattended? _____

   _____

9. Why is it dangerous to leave a reaction unattended while heating it?

   _____

10. Why is smoking forbidden in the laboratory? _____

    _____

11. a) What is a "contained" fire? _____

    _____

    b) What is a simple method to put out a small "contained" fire?

    _____

12. a) What can be used to smother a clothing fire? _____

    b) Where is it?_____

13. a) What should be used to put out an open fire in the laboratory?_____

_____

b) Where are they?_____

_____

14. Describe the steps of using a fire extinguisher.

a) _____   b) _____

c) _____   d) _____

e) _____

15. Why must long hair, neckties, scarves, etc. be secured or tied back in the laboratory?

_____

16. What is the safest type of clothing recommended for wear in the laboratory?_____

_____

_____

17. What is the safest type of footwear recommended for wear in the laboratory?_____

_____

18. Why is eating and/or drinking not permissible in the laboratory?_____

_____

_____

19. What do you do with excess chemicals? Briefly describe the procedures for

a) non-hazardous liquids_____

_____

b) non-hazardous solids _____

_____

c) hazardous substances _____

_____

d) odorous substances_____

_____

e) recyclable materials _____

_____

20. Why should reagents not be

a) stored in your drawer? _____

b) taken from the laboratory?_____

21. What precautions have to be taken before using any kind of glassware from your drawer?

_____

22. Where do you dispose of broken glass?_____

_____

23. Why must balances and weighing areas be kept clean?

A)_____

B)_____

24. When is it necessary to work under a ventilation hood?_____

_____

25. What is the proper procedure to note the odor of a substance?_____

_____

26. Why must chemical reagents be added cautiously? _____

_____

27. How do you dilute concentrated acids? (What is the order of mixing?_____

_____

28. a) What is the purpose of adding a few boiling stones or chips to liquids to be heated?

_____

b) When do you add the boiling stones or chips to liquids to be heated?

_____

29. If a test tube cannot be heated in a water bath you may have to heat it over an open flame.

a) How do you hold the test tube? _____

b) How full should it be? _____

c) Where should the opening be pointed?_____

d) Where in the flame is it held?_____

e) Do you hold it stationary or in motion _____

30. What should you do in case of a power failure, fire drill, or any emergency as such?

_____

_____

_____   _____   _____
Instructor's Name   **Course**   **Section**

J: CERTIFICATION STATEMENT

THIS STATEMENT MUST BE SIGNED AND RETURNED TO YOUR LABORATORY INSTRUCTOR BEFORE YOU WILL BE PERMITTED TO WORK IN THE CHEMISTRY LABORATORY.

DEPARTMENT OF CHEMISTRY
COMMUNITY COLLEGE OF PHILADELPHIA

Print Name _____

Student ID Number _____

Course Number _____

Lecture Instructor _____

Laboratory Instructor _____

DO YOU HAVE ANY EXISTING MEDICAL CONDITION? _____YES _____NO

IF YES, EXPLAIN_____

_____

CONTACT IN CASE OF EMERGENCY _____
                                    (Name)

                        _____
                                (Phone Number)

I hereby certify that I have read, heard the safety lecture and seen the instructor's demos concerning "SAFETY RULES" in the Chemistry Laboratory. I agree to observe these at all times while taking my Chemistry course and while in the Chemistry Laboratory.

Signature _____ Date_____

The Chemistry Notebook

The "Notebook" is designed to be a PERMANENT, ACCURATE, and SIMULTANEOUS reporting of all laboratory work. To do this several things are inherently REQUIRED.

1... The notebook must be bound (i.e. sewn) so that pages CANNOT and WILL NOT be removed. Loose-leaf and spiral bindings are not permitted. [The keeping of DUPLICATE notebooks will result in an immediate grade of "F".]

2... All entries MUST be in **INK**. Pencil is NOT permitted. Errors should be XXXed out or lined out but NEVER erased. The effect on the overall neatness of the notebook due to this requirement is anticipated.

3... A TABLE OF CONTENTS (showing title of experiment and page number of write up in that **notebook**) should be provided on the first pages (1 to 2) of the notebook. Thus, ALL **notebook** pages should be NUMBERED.

4... YOUR INSTRUCTOR WILL PROVIDE SPECIFICS.
A standard format should be followed in your experimental write-ups using the RIGHT hand pages ONLY. Reserve the left hand pages for fast notes, math calculations, etc. (See details to follow: but in general:

- The experiment's TITLE, PURPOSE, THEORY and PROCEDURE must be entered into your notebooks **before** you come to **lab**.
- DATA TABLES must also be set up **in advance** for ease in recording your data.
- The experiment's DATE, PARTNER (if any), DATA, and OBSERVATIONS will be recorded while you are in lab. Your "data" is any pertinent measurement you make and/or record. "Observations" should include anything you detect via your senses.
- A CONCLUSION with DISCUSSION and ERROR ANALYSIS must be completed for each experiment to finish off the report. This is usually done at home **after** the experiment has been completed.

COMMUNITY COLLEGE OF PHILADELPHIA
DEPARTMENT OF CHEMISTRY
POLICY CONCERNING ACADEMIC DISHONESTY

American higher education and science have an old and strong tradition of honesty. There is no room in academia or in science for cheating or any other type of academic dishonesty. Many of the nation's universities and colleges rely on an honor system concerning examinations; to be found cheating during an examination is the basis for immediate expulsion. The Department of Chemistry at Community College of Philadelphia subscribes to this treatment of those who cheat.

Cheating may be defined as (a) looking at another student's examination paper, (b) askinganother student for any type of help during an examination, (c) bringing notes of any type to an examination, (d) plagiarizing work done by another without giving full credit, (e) falsification of information including laboratory data, (f) lying, (g) making notes during an examination onscrap paper to give to another student, (h) stealing an examination, (i) asking another person for helpon take-home examinations, (j) writing notes on desk tops, (k) passing calculators that contain information to another student, (l) changing answers on an examination after it has been returned, and (m) having another student take an examination for you. Any of these violations constitutes a highly serious offense, which will ultimately result in some type of disciplinary action.

Persons properly trained in science, perhaps more so than the general public, find scientific and academic cheating highly offensive. How can one trust the laboratory data or scientific findings of a person known to cheat? Will this person make an honest physician or dentist? Will this person make an honest pharmacist? Does this person or this person's work have any integrity? One single instance of cheating can cast doubt on everything that person does, and it can follow one for a lifetime.

Students caught cheating will find that it may result in (a) refusal to accept you back into the course, (b) your name will be reported to the Dean of Students, and to the Vice President for Academic Affairs, with the recommendation that you be expelled from the college. If you are not expelled, all of your present and subsequent professors will be notified of your academic dishonesty. Last, you will never receive any letter of recommendation from any Community College of Philadelphia chemistry faculty member.

Now think it over, is cheating worth the risk of having the above happen to you? If you think these things won't happen, you are sadly mistaken. You will find out the hard way.

The great majority of students are honest, and cheating is not usually a problem. We apologize to those of you who work honestly, that we have found it necessary to write this statement because of a few who are dishonest.

Kathleen A. Harter
Professor and Chair, Department of Chemistry

Unanimously adopted at a meeting of the Department, March 1992

MATH SKILLS NEEDED FOR CHEMISTRY 110

TOPIC	PROCESS	COMMENT
1. Simple manipulation on the calculator	Addition, Subtraction Multiplication & Division	Used throughout the course
2. Signed numbers	Algebraic addition and subtraction	Used in exponential manipulation oxidation numbers, formula writing
3. Equation manipulation	Solving simple equations for one unknown	Used in density, calorimetry, and gas problems
4. Exponential notation	Changing decimals to expontentials and the reverse; multiplying & dividing exponents	Used in measurement and stoichiometry
5. Introduction to metric system	Use of milli-, centi-, kilo-, & mega- in length, volume and mass measurements	Used throughout the lab and the course
6. Dimensional Analysis	Converting one unit into a different unit	Used in density, measurement, stoichiometry and gas problems
7. Physical measurement	Reading the balance, meter stick and graduated cylinder	Used in experiments

EXAMPLES OF MATH USED IN CHEMISTRY 110

A.   Using your calculator

1. Add   3.573 and 5.395

2. Subtract   4.764 from 2.468

3. Multiply   6.638 by 9.473

4. Divide   7.269 by 8.483

B.   Add these numbers on your calculator

5. -47.692 and +23.855

6. +53.721 and –97.016

C.   Solve for the term indicated

7.   If   FG = HJ   then G =

8.   If $\dfrac{K}{L} = \dfrac{M}{N}$ then K =

9.   If $\dfrac{OR}{U} = \dfrac{ST}{V}$ then U =

10. If   WX = YZA   then Y =

D.   Solve using a calculator

11.   0.00681 multiplied by 6.71×10^{-5}

12. 8.3×10^{7} divided by 0.00026

E.   What metric unit would be most appropriate to measure the following?

13.   The thickness of a half dollar

14.   The weight of a teaspoon of sugar

F. Convert

        15. 3267 mm to m
        16. 8575 kg to g

G. Solve

        17. If one ounce of gold costs $385, how many ounces of gold can be purchased for $678,592?

        18. If one candy bar contains 2.53 grams of sugar, how many grams of sugar are contained in 9653 candy bars?

Answer Key

A   1. 8.968
       2. -2.296
       3. 62.88
       4. 0.8569

B.   5. -23.837
       6. -43.295

C.   7. $G = \dfrac{HJ}{F}$

       8. $K = \dfrac{ML}{N}$

       9. $U = \dfrac{ORV}{ST}$

       10. $Y = \dfrac{WX}{ZA}$

D.   11. 4.57×10^{-7}

       12. $3.2 \times 10^{+11}$

E.   13. millimeter or mm
       14. gram or g

F.   15. 3.267 m
       16. 8,575,000g

G.   17. $1.76 \times 10^{+3}$ oz
       18. $2.44 \times 10^{+4}$g

Introduction to Laboratory Measurements

OBJECTIVE

To become familiar with common measuring devices used in a laboratory; to learn the sensitivity with which these devices can be used; and to gain an appreciation for the degree of uncertainty associated with data obtained in the lab.

APPARATUS AND CHEMICALS

burets with stands	metal object
100-mL graduated cylinder	thermometers
10-mL graduated cylinder	calculator
50-mL beaker	burner
400-mL beaker	ring
copper wire or paperclip	ring stand
tongs	wire gauze
meter stick	clamp
balance	one-hole, split rubber stopper

SAFETY CONSIDERATIONS

 Use care in handling the graduated cylinder. While laboratory glassware is made of durable glass, it can shatter if mishandled, and can cause severe cuts.

 No immediate eye danger is present in this particular experiment, but as a part of your introduction to the lab you should be made aware that *safety glasses are to be worn at all times* in the lab.

 Mercury is poisonous and can be absorbed through the skin. A broken thermometer can splatter mercury in the working area.

 When using a burner or any open flame in the laboratory, be absolutely sure that loose hair and clothing do not come close to the flame. Many hair sprays contain highly flammable components that cause hair to burn quickly. Long hair should be tightly tied back in the lab. It is easy to forget these simple rules when concentrating on measurements.

 Be sure the gas is turned off completely when you are through with it since in a closed laboratory a small gas leak can build up to an explosive mixture.

FACTS TO KNOW

Much of what is done in a chemistry lab involves taking measurements on a system using appropriate measuring devices, and then making calculations with the numbers obtained. Numbers used in such calculations fall into two broad categories: pure numbers and estimated numbers. Pure numbers are those with no uncertainty at all. These include small numbers of *counted* items (the number of eggs in a nest or puppies in a particular litter, for example) and *defined* numbers (3 feet in 1 yard, 16 ounces in 1 pound, for example). In each case, the numbers are generally written as whole numbers, but could be written correctly to any number of places (3 feet = 1 yard, or 3.00 feet = 1.00 yard). It is the other category of numbers—estimated (measured) numbers—with which chemists deal most frequently.

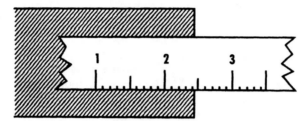

Figure 1-1. Estimation of length as 2.43.

Most measuring devices have some sort of scale to be read. The scales will have individual marks, called graduation marks, and will have printed numbers at regular positions along the marks. The proper way to use such a scale is to **record the measured value to one more place than the scale is marked.** For instance, if using a meter stick that is marked in millimeters (mm), record the length to 0.1 mm. With a cylinder graduated in milliliters (mL), record the value to 0.1 mL. The last place in the number is **your best estimate** of the fractional part of the graduation. For example, in Figure 1-1, it can easily be seen that the value of the reading falls between 2 and 3, and, by counting graduations, that it falls between 2.4 and 2.5. One can *estimate* that the reading falls about 3/10 of the way between the finest graduations, giving a measurement of 2.43. The last number *could* be a 2 or a 4, but the measurement is certainly much closer to 2.43 than to 2.4 or 2.5. The best way to record such a reading would be 2.43 ± .01 to show reasonable limits of uncertainty. In this case, the actual value is probably within 0.5% of the measured value, and this can be easily seen by anyone who examines the number. When calculations must be done with numbers obtained through measurements taken in a laboratory, it is very important to know the degree of uncertainty in the measured values. This is done through the use of **significant digits,** that is, figures in which the uncertainty is only in the *last recorded digit* (for example, the 3 in the recorded number 2.43 discussed above).

EXAMPLE 1

Fourteen cherries are placed in a pre-weighed bowl and found to have a total weight of 21.17 grams. What is the average weight of a cherry, to the correct number of significant digits?

Answer: The 14 is a pure or exact number and has an unlimited number of significant figures. The weight is a measured number and contains uncertainty (estimate) in the fourth significant digit. Thus, the answer will have the same degree of uncertainty as the *least* certain of the numbers being divided, or: (21.17 grams)/(14 cherries) = 1.512 grams/cherry. (Note, the position of the decimal *does not matter* as far as the number of significant digits is concerned.)

When multiplying or dividing groups of measured values the answer will have the same number of significant digits as the least accurately known (fewest significant digits) of the numbers being multiplied or divided.

EXAMPLE 2

Using a balance, a student determines the mass of an object to be 12.37 ± 0.02 grams. She then uses a graduated cylinder and measures the object's volume to be 3.12 ± 0.02 cm^3. What is the density of the object, reported to the correct number of significant figures, and how could one show WHY there is a "correct" number of significant figures?

Answer: The object's density, calculated using these numbers *and ignoring significant figures* is 3.96474 g/cm^3. The ± 0.02 numbers represent reasonable uncertainty in reading the scales. Thus, while the *best estimate* for the mass was 12.37 g, it could reasonably have any value between 12.35 g and 12.39 g, while the volume could reasonably have any value between 3.10 cm^3 and 3.14 cm^3.

(a) Treating the *mass as a pure number* (no uncertainty) and the volume as a measured number produces a range of densities from 3.9395 g/cm^3 to 3.9903 g/cm^3 (dividing 12.37 by 3.14, then dividing 12.37 by 3.10). This is a variation of 0.0508 g/cm^3.

(b) Treating the *volume as a pure number* (no uncertainty) and the mass as a measured number produces a range of densities from 3.9583 g/cm^3 to 3.9712 g/cm^3 (dividing 12.35 by 3.12, then dividing 12.39 by 3.12). This is a variation of only 0.0129 g/cm^3.

As can be seen in the above comparison, the uncertainty in volume causes an uncertainty in the final result that is 4 times as great as the uncertainty in the same calculation caused by the uncertainty in mass. This is because there are four significant figures in the mass, and only three significant figures in the volume. The *actual* uncertainty incorporates both figures and could be estimated by comparing the (low)/(high) and the (high)/(low) figures. In the above example, these would be 12.35/3.14 (3.9395 g/cm^3) and 12.39/3.10 (3.9968 g/cm^3), or a total uncertainty of 0.0573 g/cm^3. Note the closeness of this value to that produced by the uncertainty in volume alone (in (a) above)! The correct value for the answer to this calculation would be 3.96 g/cm^3 (three significant figures). **The answer will contain only 3 significant figures, since the volume contained only 3 significant figures.**

EXAMPLE 3

A boy weighs his pet hamster on a laboratory balance and finds that it weighs 125.23 grams. He then weighs a sample of hamster food on an analytical balance and finds that it weighs 0.1273 grams. The hamster immediately eats the food, with no leftovers. What is the new weight of the hamster?

Answer: The 3 in 125.23 is *estimated*. It could be a 2 or a 4 or possibly a 1 or a 5. For this reason, it does not do any good to know the weight of the food to any *greater* accuracy than the hundredths place when adding it, since there will be uncertainty here anyway. Thus, *round off* the 0.1273 to 0.13 (125.23 + 0.13 = 125.36 g). The uncertainty is still in the hundredths place.

When adding or subtracting numbers, the answer is significant only to the fewest number of decimal places contained in any of the numbers being added or subtracted.

A second and equally important consideration of recording and using numbers is that virtually *all* numbers encountered in the laboratory represent quantities associated with *a specific material or phenomenon*. This means that value of the number is inseparably tied to the dimensions (frequently called "units") in which the quantity is measured. Suppose you were given the mass (or weight) of an object as 12, and asked how many of these you could carry. It makes a great difference whether the quantity is 12 milligrams, 12 grams, 12 ounces, 12 pounds, 12 kilograms, or 12 tons! **MEASURED NUMBERS ARE MEANINGLESS UNLESS THE PROPER DIMENSION (UNIT) ACCOMPANIES THE NUMBER. THESE DIMENSIONS (UNITS) ARE RETAINED IN CALCULATIONS.**

EXAMPLE 4

Seven corks weigh 28.23 grams. What is the average weight of a single cork?

Answer: (28.23 grams)/(7 corks) = 4.033 g/cork. Note that the 28.23 is a measured number and the 7 is a pure or exact number, so that there will be 4 significant figures in the answer. Many students find it helpful to verbalize the slash in the units as the words "for every." Thus, 4.033 g/cork would be read as 4.033 grams *for every* cork.

PROCEDURE

Numbers in parentheses refer to entry numbers on the data sheet.

This lab experience is designed to allow the student to become familiar with several common measuring devices which will be used throughout the course, and to develop an understanding of the inherent uncertainty in measuring with each. You will go into the lab and take measurements at stations which have been set up by your instructor before the lab. You will use the data for some simple calculations with a calculator. The class will then, as a whole, compare data to see where the numbers agree and where they disagree.

 I. GRADUATED CYLINDERS are glassware designed to transfer quickly a fairly accurately measured volume of liquid into another container and should not be used where *highly* accurate measurements are required.

Read the level of the meniscus (dividing line between water and air—your instructor will demonstrate the proper technique) for each graduated cylinder (1 and 2). Notice that the meniscus is curved at the middle (Fig. 1-2). The lowest point on this curve, not the upper edge, is always read as the volume. Avoid errors due to parallax; different readings are obtained if the eye's line of sight is not perpendicular to the scale.

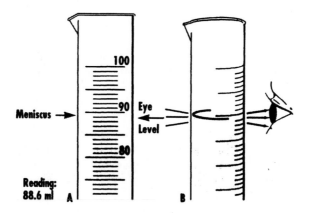

Figure 1-2. How to read a graduated cylinder.

II. BURETS are glassware designed to deliver conveniently a *very accurately* measured quantity of liquid into another container. The volume delivered is equal to the difference in the final and initial level readings. Read the liquid level in each of the three burets (3, 4, and 5) to the nearest 0.01 mL.

 III. THERMOMETERS are devices used to measure temperature. A *thermometer* will be used to measure the temperature of boiling water that is heated by a laboratory burner. Examine the burner and locate the gas and air valves (Fig. 1-3). Operate each valve before attaching the burner to the gas outlet. Close off the air and gas valves, attach hose to gas outlet on the burner and the desk, and open the desk valve about three-fourths of the way.

Strike a match and, while holding the lighted match to the side and just below the top of the barrel of the burner, gradually open the gas valve on the burner until a flame about 3 or 4 inches high is obtained. Now gradually open the air valve until a blue flame with an inner cone is obtained. Holding a piece of copper wire or a paper clip in the flame with tongs, locate the hottest and coolest parts of the flame by the degree of light shown by the copper. Is the hottest part of the flame at the top of the burner, in the middle of the blue flame, or at the top of the blue flame (6)?

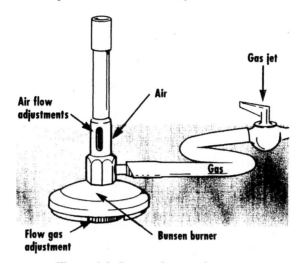

Figure 1-3. Bunsen burner features.

Set up a beaker on a wire gauze on an iron ring (Fig. 1-4). Fill the beaker about half full with water. Adjust your burner to give medium temperature and begin heating with water. Time can be saved if the water is heated while other parts of the experiment are being done. Periodically determine the temperature of the water with the thermometer. Be sure the mercury bulb is in the water, and be careful not to touch the walls of the beaker with the thermometer bulb. Record the boiling point of the water (7).

IV. BEAKERS are glassware designed for handling liquids (heating, reactions, etc.). The graduations are only *approximate*, and beakers are not designed as accurate measuring devices. Estimate the level of water in each beaker (8 and 9).

V. METER STICKS measure distance. Record the length of the object *in mm* (10).

VI. BALANCES are used in the laboratory for determining mass. Your instructor will demonstrate the use of the balance you are to use. You will determine the mass of an object with the balance, then determine the volume of the object by displacement, using a graduated cylinder. This mass divided by the volume gives its density, which is a physical characteristic of the substance. Weigh the object (11).

Fill a 100-mL graduated cylinder about half full of water and record the volume (12). Then carefully tilt the cylinder and slide the metal object down the side (to minimize splashing) and record the new liquid level (13). The metal must be completely submerged in the water. The difference in readings is the volume of the metal object (14).

Use a calculator to calculate the density of the object (15). Density = mass/volume. Also use a calculator to perform the mathematical operations listed at the bottom of the data sheet.

As your instructor indicates, read aloud the number you have recorded for each station, **exactly as you have recorded it.** Tables will be made for each station (one showing the complete calculator reading and the other showing the correctly rounded values). Note the range of measured values for each station. Comment on the "correct" value from these various tables (16). Compare the tables of calculated and rounded values. How do the correctly rounded values correlate with the total calculator readings (17)?

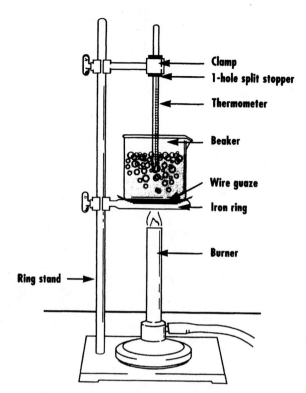

Clamp

1-hole split stopper

Thermometer

Beaker

Wire guaze

Iron ring

Burner

Ring stand

Figure 1-4. Set-up for thermometer bath.

PRE-LAB QUESTIONS

1. Under what circumstances is hair spray a laboratory hazard, as described in the **SAFETY CONSIDERATIONS** section?

    _____

    _____

    _____

    _____

    _____

    _____

2. Two students, working together, are asked to determine the average mass of a single cork in a bag of corks. One student determines the number of corks in the bag and the other student weighs the corks, so that the weight of all the corks can be divided by the number of corks. Comment on the *fundamental difference* in the nature of the numbers that each student obtained

    _____

    _____

    _____

    _____

    _____

    _____

3. Arrange the following in **increasing order** of the accuracy of the measurements which may be made with their graduation marks.

    buret, beaker, graduated cylinder

    _____ < _____ < _____

4. In only two parts of this laboratory procedure will the student actually perform operations *other than* reading scales that have been previously setup. What quantities are being measured in each of these instances?

    (1) _____

    (2) _____

INTRODUCTION TO LABORATORY MEASUREMENTS

graduated cylinders

(1) _____ mL

(2) _____ mL

beakers

(8) _____ mL

(9) _____ mL

burets

(3) _____ mL

(4) _____ mL

(5) _____ mL

length of object

(10) _____ mm

mass

(11) _____ g

thermometers

(6) _____

(7) _____ °C

(12) Initial cylinder level   _____ mL

(13) Final cylinder level   _____ mL

(14) Volume (subtract 12 from 13)   _____ mL

(15) Density (divide 11 by 14)   _____ g/mL (g/cm^3)

Calculations

Record both the calculator reading and the correctly rounded value.

a) Volume of 400-mL beaker + volume of 100-mL cylinder (8 + 9)

calculator number _____ rounded number _____

b) Volume of buret (3) × length of object (10)

calculator number _____ rounded number _____

c) mass (11) ÷ length of object (10)

calculator number _____ rounded number _____

d) Volume of buret (5) × Volume of buret (3)

calculator number _____ rounded number _____

e) Density of metal object (15)

calculator number _____ rounded number _____

When each member of the class has performed the above calculations, the results will be collected into tables for examination.

(16) _____

_____

_____

(17) _____

_____

_____

POST-LAB QUESTIONS

1. Determine the correct answers to the calculation shown below *to the correct number of significant figures.*

   (a) $(32.453)(34.23 + 1.17)/(2.26 - 1.811)(0.00378) =$ _____

   (b) $(3.23 + 0.0018) =$ _____

   (c) $(82.97 - 0.012)/(1.100)(21.9) =$ _____

2. How many significant figures are in each of the following measurements, which have been taken with the indicated device?

   (a) 430 mL (beaker) _____

   (b) 237.35 g (triple beam balance) _____

   (c) 34.20 mL (buret) _____

Densities of Liquids and Solids

Performance Goal

2–1   Calculate the density of a liquid or a solid from experimental data.

CHEMICAL OVERVIEW

One of the physical properties that characterize a substance is its **density,** which is defined as its *mass per unit volume.* Mathematically,

$$\text{Density} = \frac{\text{mass}}{\text{volume}} \qquad (2.1)$$

According to this equation, density is equal to the ratio of the mass of a sample of a substance to the volume it occupies. The density of a solid is normally expressed in grams per cubic centimeter (g/cm^3), the density of a liquid in grams per cubic centimeter or grams per milliliter (g/mL), and the density of a gas in grams per liter (g/L).

To determine the density of a substance you must measure both the mass and volume of the same sample of the substance. Density is then calculated by dividing the mass by the volume, as indicated in Equation 2.1. Mass is measured by the usual weighing techniques. The volume of a liquid may be measured in a graduated cylinder. The dimensions of a solid with a regular geometric shape (rectangular block, cylinder, sphere) may be measured with a ruler, and these measurements can then be used to calculate the volume. The volume of a solid with an irregular shape may be determined by measuring the volume of a liquid displaced when the solid is immersed in the liquid.

In Part 1 of this experiment you will be asked to determine experimentally the density of a known substance and then to calculate the **percent error** in your determination. Percent error is defined by the following equation:

$$\text{Percent error} = \frac{\text{error}}{\text{accepted value}} \times 100 \qquad (2.2)$$

The "error" is the difference between the experimental value and the accepted value. Error is expressed as an **absolute value,** i.e., a numerical value without regard for algebraic sign. Absolute value is indicated by enclosing the quantity between vertical lines. Thus Equation 5.2 becomes

$$\text{Percent error} = \frac{|\text{experimental value} - \text{accepted value}|}{\text{accepted value}} \times 100 \qquad (2.3)$$

SAFETY PRECAUTIONS AND DISPOSAL METHODS

Safety hazards in this experiment cannot be identified precisely because of the wide variety of chemicals that might be used as liquid unknowns. This uncertainty dictates that all liquids be regarded as potentially dangerous and treated accordingly. This includes the known liquid, trichloroethane. Liquid samples should be obtained from a dispensing station in the hood. If taken from the hood, liquids should be in containers that are stoppered or covered with a plastic sheet or metal foil. Some unknowns may be flammable; they should therefore be kept away from open flames. When you are finished with them, discard them as directed by your instructor. Avoid contact between all liquids and your skin; if it occurs, wash the exposed area thoroughly with soap and water. *Safety glasses must be worn at all times.*

Depending on the nature of your liquid unknown, disposal directions will be given by your instructor. Trichloroethane should be collected in a stoppered bottle.

PROCEDURE

Note: All mass measurements are to be recorded in grams to the nearest 0.01 g. Length measurements are to be recorded in centimeters to the nearest 0.1 cm. Record liquid volume measurements in milliliters to the nearest 0.1 mL.

1. DENSITY OF A LIQUID

A)   Your 50-mL graduated cylinder and a piece of plastic wrap (e.g. Saran wrap) to cover the opening constitute your "container" for Part 1 of this experiment. Being sure the cylinder is clean and dry, weigh it and the Saran wrap — the container — to the nearest 0.01 g on a centigram balance. Record the mass in the proper number of significant figures on your report sheet.

B)   Take the cylinder and plastic wrap to the hood. Pour 12 to 15 mL of 1,1,1-trichloroethane into the cylinder; do *not* attempt to make the amount *exactly* 12, 13, 14, or 15 mL. Cover the cylinder with the plastic wrap. Estimate the volume to the nearest 0.1 mL, and record that value to the proper number of significant figures.

C)   After making sure the outside of the cylinder is dry, measure and record the mass of the container plus liquid on the centigram balance.

D)   Dispose of your liquid as directed by your instructor.

E)   In the same manner, collect data for finding the densities of one or more unknown liquids, as required by your instructor. *Be sure to record the identification number of each unknown.*

2. DENSITY OF A REGULAR SOLID

Select one or more of the solid unknowns provided for this experiment and record its identification number. Determine and record its mass to the nearest centigram. Make whatever measurements may be necessary to calculate the volume of the object, listing these measurements to the closest 0.1 cm. Because these objects are of various shapes, the data table contains blank spaces in which to describe the shapes and identify the measurements (length, diameter, etc.) that are made.

3. DENSITY OF AN IRREGULAR SOLID

A)   Place 20 to 25 mL of water into the cylinder from Part 1. Record the volume to the nearest 0.1 mL. Determine the mass of the cylinder plus water to the nearest centigram. This is the mass of the container for Part 3.

B)   Select and record the identification number of one of the unknown irregular solids provided for this experiment. Place enough of the solid into the graduated cylinder to cause the liquid level to rise by more than 10 milliliter markings. Be sure all of the solid is below the surface of the liquid. Record the volume to the nearest 0.1 mL. Also measure the mass of the container and its contents to the nearest centigram.

C)   Dispose of your solid material into the recovery facility that has been set up in your laboratory. Be careful not to mix unknown solids.

D)   Repeat Steps 3A and 3B for as many unknowns as are required by your instructor, or for a second run with the same unknown.

CALCULATIONS

Be sure to include units in the results of all calculations. Also be sure to express those results in the correct number of significant figures.

1. DENSITY OF A LIQUID

Find the mass of the liquid by difference — by subtracting the mass of the container from the mass of the container plus liquid. The density of the liquid is found by dividing the mass of the liquid sample by its volume, as indicated in Equation 2.1. Percent error may be calculated by substituting into Equation 2.3; be careful of significant figures in the result. The accepted value for the density of 1,1,1-trichloroethane is 1.34 g/mL.

2. DENSITY OF A REGULAR SOLID

The volume of a rectangular solid is calculated by multiplying the length by the width by the height: $V = l \times w \times h$.

The volume of a cylinder is the area of the base times the height. The area of a circle is $\pi d^2/4$, where d is the diameter. Thus

$$V_{cylinder} = \frac{\pi d^2 h}{4}$$

The value of π to eight decimal places is 3.14159265; the number of places to which you should round it off is left to you.

The volume of a sphere is found from the following equation:

$$V_{sphere} = \frac{\pi d^3}{6}$$

Once you have calculated the volume of the unknown solid, its density may be found by substituting into Equation 2.1, as before.

3. DENSITY OF AN IRREGULAR SOLID

Both the mass and the volume of the sample are found by difference. Density is again calculated by substitution into Equation 2.1.

Work Page

1) DENSITY OF A LIQUID

Liquid (List identification number of unknowns)	Trichlorethane			
Mass of container + liquid (g)				
Mass of container (g)				
Mass of liquid (g)				
Volume of liquid (mL)				
Density (g/mL)				
Percent error (trichloroethane only)				

"Accepted" value for density of 1,1,1-trichloroethane: 1.34 g/mL.

Calculation Setups for Density Determinations:

Calculation Setups for Percent Error for Trichloroethane:

2) DENSITY OF A REGULAR SOLID

Unknown Number				
Shape of unknown				
Volume of unknown (cm³)				
Mass of unknown (g)				
Density (g/cm³)				

Calculation Setups for Determination of Volumes of Unknowns:

For each unknown, list the measurements taken and show calculation setup.

Calculation Setups for Density Determinations:

Work Page

3) DENSITY OF AN IRREGULAR SOLID

Unknown Number				
Mass of container + liquid + solid (g)				
Mass of container + liquid (g)				
Mass of solid (g)				
Volume of liquid + solid (mL)				
Volume of liquid (mL)				
Volume of solid (cm^3)				
Density (g/cm^3)				

Calculation Setups for Density Determinations:

Report Sheet

1) DENSITY OF A LIQUID

Liquid (List identification number of unknowns)	Trichlorethane			
Mass of container + liquid (g)				
Mass of container (g)				
Mass of liquid (g)				
Volume of liquid (mL)				
Density (g/mL)				
Percent error (trichloroethane only)				

"Accepted" value for density of 1,1,1-trichloroethane: 1.34 g/mL.

Calculation Setups for Density Determinations:

Calculation Setups for Percent Error for Trichloroethane:

2) DENSITY OF A REGULAR SOLID

Unknown Number				
Shape of unknown				
Volume of unknown (cm³)				
Mass of unknown (g)				
Density (g/cm³)				

Calculation Setups for Determination of Volumes of Unknowns:

For each unknown, list the measurements taken and show calculation setup.

Calculation Setups for Density Determinations:

Report Sheet

3) DENSITY OF AN IRREGULAR SOLID

Unknown Number				
Mass of container + liquid + solid (g)				
Mass of container + liquid (g)				
Mass of solid (g)				
Volume of liquid + solid (mL)				
Volume of liquid (mL)				
Volume of solid (cm^3)				
Density (g/cm^3)				

Calculation Setups for Density Determinations:

Advance Study Assignment

1) The volume of an unknown liquid is 28.6 mL and its mass is 32.2 grams. Calculate the density of the liquid.

2) When 95.0 g of an unknown metal are submerged in water in a graduated cylinder, the water level rises from 38.2 mL to 49.5 mL. Calculate the density of the metal.

3) The accepted value for the density of a certain metal is 5.48 g/cm^3. Calculate the percent error in a laboratory experiment that yields a value of 5.2 g/cm^3. Express this result in the proper number of significant figures.

Experiment 3 Ⓜ

Separation of Cations by Paper Chromatography

Performance Goals

3–1 Separate a mixture of cations by paper chromatography and calculate their R_F values.
3–2 Analyze an unknown mixture of cations by paper chromatography.

CHEMICAL OVERVIEW

Chromatography, which means "the graphing of colors," gets its name from the early experiments of Tswett, who, in 1906, succeeded in separating a mixture of colored pigments obtained from leaves. A solvent mixture, carrying the pigments, was allowed to pass through a glass column packed with chalk. At the end of the experiment, the pigments were separated in colored bands at various distances from the starting level. This method is now known as column chromatography.

Chromatography may now be applied to colorless compounds and to ions. Paper chromatography is a more recent and much faster separation technique than column chromatography. It may be used for the separation of substances by a solvent moving on sheets or strips of filter paper. The filter paper is referred to as the **stationary phase,** or **adsorbent.** The mixture of solvents used to carry the substances along the paper is called the **mobile phase,** or **solvent system.**

In practice, a sample of the solution containing the substances to be separated is dried on the paper. The end of the paper is dipped into the solvent system so that the sample to be analyzed is slightly above the liquid surface. As the solvent begins to soak the paper, rising by capillary action, it transports the sample mixture upward. Each component of the mixture being separated is held back by the stationary phase to a different extent. Also, each component has a different solubility in the mobile phase and therefore moves forward at a different speed. A combination of these effects causes each component of the mixture to progress at a different rate, resulting in separation.

In a given solvent system, using the same adsorbent at a fixed temperature, each substance can be characterized by a constant **retention factor,** R_F. By definition,

$$R_F = \frac{\text{Distance from origin to center of spot}}{\text{Distance from origin to solvent front}} \qquad (3.1)$$

where the **origin** is the point at which the sample was originally placed on the paper and the **solvent front** is the line representing the most advanced penetration of the paper by the solvent system. The R_F value is a characteristic property of a species, just as the melting point is a characteristic property of a compound.

In this experiment you will separate a mixture of iron(III), copper(II), and cobalt(II) ions, Fe^{3+}, Cu^{2+}, and Co^{2+}, respectively. Each ion forms a different colored complex when sprayed with a solution containing potassium hexacyano ferrate(II), $K_4[Fe(CN)_6]$.

SAFETY PRECAUTIONS AND DISPOSAL METHODS

Acetone is *extremely flammable.* Its vapors can ignite even when the liquid is a considerable distance from an open flame, so be sure no such flame is operating in the vicinity of your work area. Fumes of acetone and concentrated hydrochloric acid are objectionable and, to some degree, harmful. These chemicals should be used in the hood. Be sure to wear safety glasses.

After you have finished the experiment, dispose of the solvent mixture in a stoppered bottle.

PROCEDURE

1. Using a graduated cylinder and working in the hood, prepare the following solvent system: 19 mL acetone; 4 mL concentrated hydrochloric acid, HCl; 2 mL water or use 25 mL of a pre-prepared solvent mixture, if available. Pour the solvent mixture into an 800- or 1000-mL beaker and cover it tightly with a plastic film (e.g., Saran wrap). This allows the atmosphere within the beaker to become saturated with solvent vapor and helps to give a better chromatographic separation.

2. Obtain a piece of chromatography paper 24 to 25 cm long by 11 to 14 cm wide. Draw a pencil line about 1 cm from the long edge of the paper. (You must use an ordinary pencil for this line. Ink or colored pencil often contains substances that may be soluble in the solvent, producing chromatograms of their own.) This line will indicate the origin (see Figure 3–1). Also draw a line about 1 cm long, 6 cm above the center of the penciled line.

3. Using a different capillary tube for each solution (do not mix them!) transfer a drop of each solution listed below to the penciled line, as shown in Figure 3–1. Apply the spots evenly over the line, leaving a margin of about 3 cm from each short edge of the paper. Use a separate, clean capillary tube for each solution; or, if the solutions are to be obtained from beakers in which a capillary tube is provided, *be sure to return the tube to its proper beaker.* With a pencil, identify each spot by writing on the paper directly beneath the spot. The solutions are:
   A. Fe^{3+} solution
   B. Cu^{2+} solution
   C. Co^{2+} solution
   D. Solution containing all three ions, Fe^{3+}, Cu^{2+}, and Co^{2+}
   E. Any of the unknowns furnished (be sure to record its number)
   F. Another unknown (again, record the number).

4. Dry the paper under a heat lamp or air blower.

5. Form the paper into a cylinder without overlapping the edges. Fasten the paper with staples, as shown in Figure 3–2.

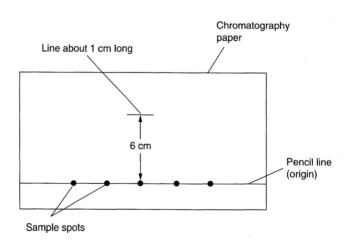

Figure 3–1. Preparing chromatography paper.

Line about 1 cm long

Chromatography paper

6 cm

Pencil line (origin)

Sample spots

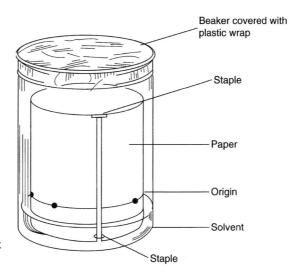

Figure 3–2. Development of chromatogram.

6. Place the beaker in a position on your desk where it will remain undisturbed throughout this step. Taking care that the origin line remains above the solvent, carefully place the cylinder into the beaker, as shown in Figure 3–2. Replace the plastic film and wait as the solvent moves up the paper. Do not move the beaker or the solvent front will be uneven.

7. *NOTE: In this and all remaining steps, when the paper is wet, be sure not to lay it down on any surface that is not clean.* When the solvent has risen above the short line drawn 6 cm above the origin in Step 2, remove the cylinder from the beaker and quickly mark the solvent front position with a pencil. Remove the staples and dry the paper under a heat lamp.

8. Spray the paper with a solution of potassium hexacyano ferrate(II), $K_4[Fe(CN)_6]$.*

   The presence of Fe^{3+} is shown by the spot turning a dark steel blue color. Cu^{2+} turns a rust brown, and Co^{2+} turns grayish purple (rose).

RESULTS AND CALCULATIONS

Observe and record on the work page the colors of spots produced by the three ions in each of the chromatograms of solutions A through D.

Measure and record in millimeters the distance between the origin and the solvent front (X in Figure 3–3). Next, measure and record the distance between the origin and the center of each spot in the chromatograms for solutions A through D. Calculate the R_F value for each ion, using Equation 3.1. Record that value as a decimal fraction to two decimals (i.e., 0.82, 0.75).

From the spots above your solutions E and F, indicate by a check mark in the table the ions present in the unknowns. Be sure to list the identification numbers of the unknowns.

If the center of a spot is right on the solvent front, the R_F value equals 1.00.

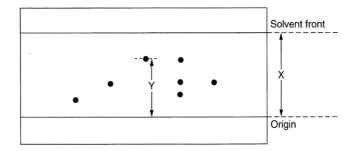

Figure 3–3. Developed chromatogram.

*Also called potassium ferrocyanide.

Advance Study Assignment

1. What would you observe if you used a ballpoint pen, instead of a pencil, to mark the chromatography paper?

2. Why do you have to cover the beaker while the solvent is moving up the paper?

3. What problem would be caused by moving the beaker during the development of the chromatogram?

4. Make the necessary measurements (in millimeters) and calculate R_F for the following chromatogram:

Work Page

Distance between origin and solvent front: _____ mm

SOLUTIONS OF KNOWN IONS

Solution	Ion	Color (After spraying)	Distance from Origin (mm)	R_F
A	Fe^{3+}			
B	Cu^{2+}			
C	Co^{2+}			
D	Fe^{3+}			
	Cu^{2+}			
	Co^{2+}			

SOLUTIONS OF UNKNOWN IONS

Put a check mark in the three right-hand columns to indicate the presence of each respective ion; leave blank if no ion is present. Be sure to enter the identification number of your unknown.

Solution	Unknown No.	Fe^{3+}	Cu^{2+}	Co^{2+}
E				
F				

Report Sheet

Distance between origin and solvent front: _____ mm

SOLUTIONS OF KNOWN IONS

Solution	Ion	Color (After spraying)	Distance from Origin (mm)	R_F
A	Fe^{3+}			
B	Cu^{2+}			
C	Co^{2+}			
D	Fe^{3+}			
	Cu^{2+}			
	Co^{2+}			

SOLUTIONS OF UNKNOWN IONS

Put a check mark in the three right-hand columns to indicate the presence of each respective ion; leave blank if no ion is present. Be sure to enter the identification number of your unknown.

Solution	Unknown No.	Fe^{3+}	Cu^{2+}	Co^{2+}
E				
F				

Calorimetry

Performance Goals

3–1 Calculate the specific heat of an unknown solid element by measuring the heat exchanged in a calorimeter.

3–2 Using the Law of Dulong and Petit, calculate the approximate atomic mass of an unknown solid element.

CHEMICAL OVERVIEW

Heat, a form of energy, can be gained or lost by an object. When the object cools, it loses heat energy; when it is heated, it gains energy. The unit in which heat is measured is the **joule, J.** A joule is a derived unit, having base units of $kg \cdot m^2/sec^2$. The joule is a very small amount of heat, so the **kilojoule, kJ,** is commonly used.*

Heat flow is the change in "heat content" of an object as heat energy passes between the object and its surroundings. It is proportional to the mass of the object and its change in temperature. The proportional relationship becomes an equation if the proportionality constant called **specific heat** is introduced:

$$Q = (mass)(specific\ heat)(\Delta T)$$
$$Q = m \times c \times \Delta T$$

(3.1)

where Q is the heat flow in joules, m is mass in grams, c is specific heat in joules per gram degree, or $J/g \cdot °C$, and ΔT is the temperature change, or final temperature minus initial temperature. The Greek letter delta, Δ, indicates a change in a measured value, and always means final value minus initial value: $\Delta X = (X_f - X_i)$.

Specific heat is a property of a pure substance. It is the number of joules of energy that are required to raise the temperature of 1 g of the substance by 1°C. The specific heat of water is 4.18 $J/g \cdot °C$. This value is used often in calorimetry experiments; it is one you should remember.

When a "hot" object comes into contact with a "cold" object — that is, when an object at higher temperature comes into contact with an object at lower temperature — heat flows from the hot object to the cold object. The hot object raises the temperature of the cold object, and the cold object cools the hot object. Eventually they reach the same intermediate temperature.

Heat flow between objects can be measured in a **calorimeter.** A perfect calorimeter is an isolated segment of the universe that allows no heat to flow to or from its contents during an experiment. It follows from the law of conservation of energy that, in a perfect calorimeter,

$$\Sigma\ Q = 0$$

(3.2)

where $\Sigma\ Q$ is the sum of all the individual changes in heat content within the calorimeter. We will assume that the calorimeters used in this experiment are "perfect." This means that any heat transferred between

---

* The joule is still in the process of replacing the calorie as the standard heat unit in chemistry, and the calorie is still in common use. The calorie is now defined as exactly 4.184 joules.

its contents and the surroundings or between its contents and the calorimeter itself are negligible and may be disregarded.

In this experiment, you will measure the specific heat of two metals, one known and the other unknown. The known metal will be copper, which has a specific heat of 0.38 J/g · °C. You will calculate the percent error from this known value. The same experimental method will be used to find the specific heat of the unknown metal.

The laboratory procedure is to heat a weighed metal sample in boiling water until it reaches the temperature of the water. This is the initial temperature of the metal. The mass and initial temperature of water in a "coffee cup" calorimeter are measured. The metal is placed into the calorimeter, and the final temperature reached by both is recorded. According to Equation 3.2, the heat flow of the metal plus the heat flow of the water add up to zero:

$$Q_w + Q_m = 0 \tag{3.3}$$

$$Q_w = -Q_m \tag{3.4}$$

What Equation 9.4 says is that the heat lost by the metal is gained by the water. Substituting the expressions of Equation 9.1 into Equation 9.4 gives

$$m_w \times c_w \times \Delta T_w = -(m_m \times c_m \times \Delta T_m) \tag{3.5}$$

All values are known except the specific heat of the metal. Note the negative sign on the right side of the equation.

The specific heat of the unknown metal will be used to estimate the atomic mass of the element, and from that you can guess its identity. This will be done with the Law of Dulong and Petit, which was proposed in 1819. In essence, this law says that the product of the specific heat and atomic mass of all solid elements is equal to 26. From this,

$$\text{Atomic mass} = \frac{26}{\text{specific heat}} \tag{3.6}$$

SAFETY PRECAUTIONS

No hazardous chemicals are used in this experiment — only hazardous temperatures. You will be working with fairly large quantities of boiling water, pouring from one container to another, and dropping pieces of metal into boiling water. Do it carefully, anticipating and avoiding the conditions that might cause you to lose control of a beaker and burn yourself or others as a result. Also in this experiment you will be working with Bunsen burners. If you have long hair, be sure to tie it back.

PROCEDURE

Note: Record all mass measurements in grams to the nearest 0.01 g. Record all temperature measurements in degrees Celsius to the nearest 0.1°C. The smallest graduation on your thermometer must be no larger than 0.2°C for satisfactory results on this experiment.

1. PREPARATION FOR CALORIMETER RUNS

A) Place about 500 mL of tap water into a beaker. Set it aside so it will come to room temperature. *Do not place it near an operating Bunsen burner.* This will be your source of calorimeter water throughout the experiment.

B) Fill a beaker, 600 mL or larger, to about 80 percent of capacity with deionized water. (The deionized water is not required from a purity standpoint, but its use avoids the buildup of hard-to-remove scale that forms when tap water is boiled in a glass vessel.) Mount the beaker over wire gauze on a ring stand and heat to boiling. Proceed to Parts C and D while waiting.

From time to time in the experiment you will have to replace the water that has boiled out of the beaker with other water *already at the boiling temperature.* If some "community" source of boiling water is not available, establish your own by setting up a second beaker in the same manner as the first.

C) Select a piece of copper and an unknown metal sample from among those provided. Record the identification number of the unknown on your data sheet. Measure the mass of each piece and record it in grams to the nearest centigram.

D) Using crucible tongs, place each piece of metal in the water being heated. Position them in such a way that they will be easy to pick up and transfer to the calorimeter later. Be careful not to drop the metal in such a manner that it hits the bottom with sufficient force to break the beaker. The metal piece should remain in the boiling water for at least 30 minutes. As you proceed with the next steps, keep watch over the water level, which must be high enough to cover the metal completely. If too much water boils away, replenish it from the community source of boiling water, or from your second beaker, as explained in B above.

E) When the water in the heating bath is boiling, determine and record its temperature to the nearest 0.1°C. Set the thermometer aside and allow it to cool to room temperature. Two assumptions are made about the temperature of the boiling water: first, that it will remain constant throughout the experiment; and second, that the metal immersed in it will reach the same temperature, which is the initial temperature of the metal for later calculations.

F) Select and prepare a place on the laboratory desk for your calorimeter runs. It should be as far as possible from an operating Bunsen burner from which it might absorb heat, but not so far that the metal loses temperature while being transferred from the boiling water to the calorimeter. It is convenient to place a split rubber stopper on your thermometer (see Figure LP–6 in the Laboratory Procedures section) and clamp it on a ring stand, or to place your thermometer in a buret clamp, as depicted in Figure 3–1.

2. FIRST CALORIMETER RUN

A) Select a polystyrene coffee cup (preferably two, one nested in the other) for your calorimeter. Weigh the cup(s) to the nearest centigram. Pour about 100 mL of your calorimeter water from Step 1A into the cup and weigh again to determine accurately the mass of water in the cup. *Do not attempt to make it exactly 100 mL.* Record the data.

B) Place the thermometer into the calorimeter water, as shown in Figure 3–1. When the temperature has remained constant for about 1 minute, record that temperature to the nearest 0.1°C. In this and all other temperature measurements, be sure the thermometer bulb is totally immersed in the water.

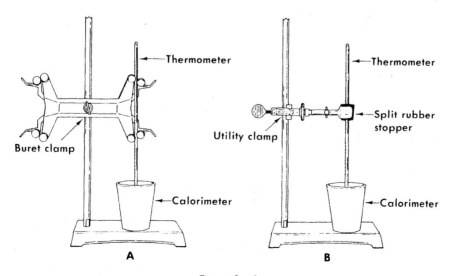

Figure 3—1

C) (*The next step is critical. The period in which the metal is out of water must be held to an absolute minimum to keep heat loss to the air as low as possible.*) Using crucible tongs, lift the piece of copper from the boiling water and hold it above the water level but below the top of the beaker for about 2 seconds to allow the boiling water to drain off. Then, *as quickly as possible,* place the metal into the calorimeter water. Be sure it is completely submerged. Be careful not to splash water out of the calorimeter. If this does occur, return the metal to the boiling water and start again at Step 2A.

D) Continuously and gently stir the water with a glass stirring rod, being careful not to break the bulb of the thermometer. Watch the thermometer. Read and record to the nearest 0.1°C the highest temperature that is reached before it begins to drop again. This may take several minutes.

E) Pour the water from the calorimeter into the sink. Place the copper back into the boiling water to be heated for a second run.

3. SUBSEQUENT CALORIMETER RUNS

Again pour about 100 mL of water into your calorimeter and weigh it to the nearest centigram. Repeat Steps 2B through 2E, using the unknown metal. The metal should be used alternately in subsequent runs, giving each sample enough time in the boiling water to reach its temperature. Make at least two runs with your copper sample and two with the unknown. At the end of the experiment, dry the metal pieces and return them to the place indicated by your instructor.

CALCULATIONS

Calculate the specific heat of the metal for each run of the experiment, using Equation 3.5, in which the specific heat is the only unknown. Find the percent error for each run with the copper, using the equations

$$\text{Percentage error} = \frac{\text{error}}{\text{accepted value}} \times 100$$

$$\text{Percentage error} = \frac{|\text{experimental value} - \text{accepted value}|}{\text{accepted value}} \times 100$$

Find the average specific heat for the two runs with the unknown metal. Estimate the atomic mass of the metal by substitution into Equation 3.6. If your estimated atomic mass is less than 100, assume your result to be correct to ±4 in the doubtful digit and record the *range* of atomic masses indicated by your experiment. For example, if your experimental value of atomic mass is 38, the indicated range is from 34 to 42. Knowing your range of atomic masses, try to identify the element that is your unknown metal. Using the 34 – 42 atomic mass range, your element could be chlorine, argon, potassium, or calcium. Other things you know about those elements should help you in selecting the most likely one as your unknown.

If your estimated atomic mass is more than 100, assume the result to be correct to ±1 in the doubtful digit and proceed as above.

Work Page

DATA

Run number					
Metal or unknown No.					
Mass of metal (g)					
Temperature of boiling water (°C)					
Mass of calorimeter (g)					
Mass of calorimeter + water (g)					
Initial temperature of calorimeter water (°C)					
Final temperature (°C)					

CALCULATIONS AND RESULTS

Record all results in the table on the following page. Show below and on the next page all calculations for one column of data and results.

CALCULATIONS AND RESULTS

Mass of water (g)					
ΔT of water (°C)					
ΔT of metal (°C)					
Heat flow (J) (absolute value)					
Specific heat (J/g · °C)					
Percent error (copper only)					
Estimated atomic mass range for unknown (amu)					
Unknown element					

Report Sheet

DATA

Run number					
Metal or unknown No.					
Mass of metal (g)					
Temperature of boiling water (°C)					
Mass of calorimeter (g)					
Mass of calorimeter + water (g)					
Initial temperature of calorimeter water (°C)					
Final temperature (°C)					

CALCULATIONS AND RESULTS

Record all results in the table on the following page. Show below and on the next page all calculations for one column of data and results.

CALCULATIONS AND RESULTS

Mass of water (g)					
ΔT of water (°C)					
ΔT of metal (°C)					
Heat flow (J) (absolute value)					
Specific heat (J/g · °C)					
Percent error (copper only)					
Estimated atomic mass range for unknown (amu)					
Unknown element					

Advance Study Assignment

1) A student places 138 g of an unknown metal at 99.6°C into 60.50 g of water at 22.1°C. The entire system reaches a uniform temperature of 31.6°C. Calculate the specific heat of the metal.

2) If the actual specific heat of the metal in Problem 1 is 0.25 J/g · °C, calculate the percentage error.

3) If, as in the example in the Calculations section, your unknown element has an atomic mass in the range of 80 to 88, which element is it most apt to be? Justify your choice.

Solution Conductivity: Covalent and Ionic Solutes

OBJECTIVES

Relate the bonding structure of substances to their behavior in solution.

Investigate the electrical conductance of various aqueous solutions.

Follow the conductance of a solution during the course of a chemical reaction.

INTRODUCTION

The known chemical and physical properties of chemical compounds can be used easily to classify the compounds into three separate groups: ionic, molecular, and metallic compounds. Members of the first group, known as the **ionic compounds**, occur as hard solids and have a distinctly crystalline appearance. Members of the first group are never found as liquids or gases at room temperature, and often result from the reaction of a metallic and a nonmetallic element. Table salt (sodium chloride) is a good example of an ionic compound.

Ionic compounds melt only at very high temperatures, often up to 1000 °C. Their boiling temperatures are even higher, and not commonly observed. Although most ionic compounds are quite soluble in water, a substantial number do not dissolve in water. Examined as solids, most ionic compounds do not conduct electricity very well and may be described as electrical insulators. When heated above their melting points, however, liquid ionic compounds are found to be good conductors of electricity. In addition, ionic compounds form electrically conducting solutions when dissolved in a suitable liquid solvent, such as water. Although neutral overall, the ionic compounds are composed of individual positively and negatively charged atoms or groups of atoms known as **ions**. Chemists often refer generically to this first group of compounds as "salts."

Members of the second group, known as **molecular compounds** or **covalent compounds**, generally melt and boil at much lower temperatures than ionic compounds. Covalent compounds are composed of individual electrically neutral molecules, and are often found as liquids or gases even at room temperature. Water is one common example, carbon dioxide a second, and sugar a third. Covalent compounds occurring as solids are relatively soft and may have either a crystalline (sugar) or an amorphous (polyethylene) appearance. Many covalent compounds undergo chemical decomposition before reaching their melting or boiling temperatures; for obvious reasons, this is called the **thermal decomposition** of the material.

Covalent compounds are electrical insulators in the solid, liquid, or gaseous state. Most covalent compounds are only sparingly soluble in water, although a significant number (sugar, grain alcohol) are quite soluble. (See Experiment Table 4.1).

The third and remaining group of compounds are **metallic compounds**. Because they generally play a minor role in the beginning study of chemistry, little more will be said of them here.

The solubility of compounds in water depends upon the ability of the polar water molecule to interact with the solute. This interaction with ionic compounds is due to strong ion–dipole attractive forces. With covalent compounds, solubility results from strong dipole–dipole attraction between solute and water molecules. Another way that a solute can dissolve in water is by reaction with water to form a soluble species. Although most covalent compounds form nonconducting solutions (alcohol in water), others form conducting solutions (carbon dioxide in water). (See Experiment Table 4.2.)

In Part I of this experiment you will investigate the electrical conductances of various aqueous solutions. These investigations will include solutions both of ionic and covalent compounds. In

EXPERIMENT TABLE 4.1 General Properties of Ionic and Molecular Compounds

Ionic compounds	Molecular compounds[a]
Crystalline solids	Gases, liquids, or solids
Hard and brittle	Solids brittle and weak, or soft and waxy
High melting points	Low melting points
High boiling points (approx. range, 700 °C to 3500 °C)	Low boiling points (approx. range, −250 °C to 600 °C)
High heats of vaporization	Low heats of vaporization
High heats of fusion	Low heats of fusion
Good conductors of electricity when molten; poor conductors of heat and electricity when solid	Poor conductors of heat and electricity
Many soluble in water	Many insoluble in water but soluble in organic solvents
Many formed by combination of reactive metals with reactive nonmetals	Many formed by combination of nonmetals with other nonmetals or with less reactive metals

[a] Many of these properties do not apply to network covalent compounds.

Part II you will follow the conductance of a solution during the course of a chemical reaction, and relate it to the disappearance of the reactants and the appearance of the products.

Substances that are electrical conductors contain electrically charged particles that are free to move throughout the substance. Such particles might be negatively charged electrons, negatively or positively charged atoms (called **simple anions** or **simple cations**), or negatively or positively charged polyatomic molecules (called **molecular anions** or **molecular cations**). This requirement

EXPERIMENT TABLE 4.2 Solubilities of Various Substances in Liquid Water

Substance			Solubility (g/100 g H_2O)	
Name	Formula	Type of Solute	20 °C	50 °C
Silver nitrate	$AgNO_3$	Ionic	222	455
Aluminum sulfate	$Al_2(SO_4)_3$	Ionic	36.4	52.2
Ammonium nitrate	NH_4NO_3	Ionic	192	344
Barium sulfate	$BaSO_4$	Ionic	2.5×10^{-4}	3.4×10^{-4}
Calcium acetate	$Ca(CH_3COO)_2$	Ionic	34.7	33.0
Copper(II) sulfate	$CuSO_4$	Ionic	20.7	33.3
Lead(II) chloride	$PbCl_2$	Ionic	0.99	1.70
Potassium chlorate	$KClO_3$	Ionic	7.4	19.3
Sodium chloride	$NaCl$	Ionic	36.0	37.0
Zinc iodide	ZnI_2	Ionic	200.	273
Hydrogen*	H_2	Nonpolar covalent	1.6×10^{-4}	1.3×10^{-4}
Ethane*	CH_3CH_3	Nonpolar covalent	0.006	0.003
Diethyl ether	$(C_2H_5)_2O$	Polar covalent	7.5	—
Ethyl alcohol	CH_3CH_2OH	Polar covalent	∞	∞
Ethylene glycol	$HOCH_2CH_2OH$	Polar covalent	∞	∞
Cane sugar	$C_{12}H_{22}O_{11}$	Polar covalent	204	260.

* Gas at 760 Torr total pressure.

for mobility prevents most solid materials (including ionic and covalent compounds) from conducting electricity. Metallic substances are prominent exceptions; they conduct electricity because their atoms pool some of their valence electrons to generate a mobile "sea" of electrons. Most ionic and covalent compounds do not show any evidence of metallic behavior and neither group conducts in the solid state.

Ionic compounds, in the solid state, are composed of charged ions that are not free to move. The ions become mobile only after they are heated to their melting temperatures, become fluid, and are freed from their fixed positions in their crystalline lattice. This large number of mobile ions then causes the molten compounds to behave as relatively good electrical conductors. The separation of the ions from each other during the melting process can be expressed as the reaction

$$MgCl_2(s) \rightarrow Mg^{2+}(l) + 2Cl^-(l)$$

Covalent compounds do not conduct electricity even when molten, because the resulting mobile particles are neutral molecules: their movement cannot be used to carry an electric charge.

Water is probably the most commonly used laboratory solvent. Water is a covalent compound exhibiting the low melting (0 °C) and boiling (100 °C) points typical of members of this group. Pure water is an extremely poor conducting liquid at room temperature. It is an unusually good solvent which dissolves many covalent and ionic compounds. Pure water is not, however, a good solvent for metallic materials.

Substances that dissolve in water to form electrically conducting solutions are called **electrolytes**. Substances that dissolve to form nonconducting solutions are known as **nonelectrolytes**. Water-soluble ionic compounds are all electrolytes. Water molecules are able to pull the positively and the negatively charged ions out of their lattice positions, completely surround the ions preventing their reprecipitation as a solid, and carry the ions along to distribute them uniformly throughout the solution. This process can be expressed as the chemical reaction

$$Ca(NO_3)_2(s) \rightarrow Ca^{2+}(aq) + 2NO_3^-(aq)$$

Most covalent compounds are nonelectrolytes. Molecules of covalent compounds are separated from each other by water molecules without the liberation of charged particles (see Experiment Figure 4.1). Some covalent compounds, however, actually react with water to form new

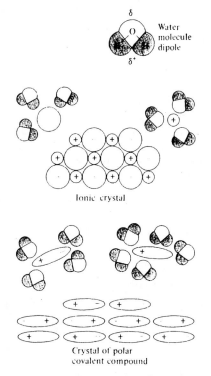

Water molecule dipole

Ionic crystal

Crystal of polar covalent compound

EXPERIMENT FIGURE 4.1 **Dissolution of Ionic and Polar Covalent Substances**

ionic species. Because such solutions do conduct electricity, these particular compounds can be called electrolytes. If all the molecules react to form ionic products, the solution becomes strongly conducting and the solutes are referred to as **strong electrolytes**. If only a fraction of the molecules react in this way, the solution becomes weakly conducting and the compound is known as a **weak electrolyte**. The following examples should clarify this difference.

The direct reaction of hydrogen gas (H_2) with chlorine gas (Cl_2) yields a covalent compound. The product of this reaction is a gas called hydrogen chloride and has the molecular formula HCl. Hydrogen chloride is extremely soluble in water, yielding a saturated solution containing approximately 12 mol HCl per liter of water at 25 °C. A liter of water contains approximately 55.6 mol of H_2O. Dissolving HCl in water yields a strongly conducting solution because of the following reaction between hydrogen chloride and water:

$$HCl(aq) + H_2O(l) \rightarrow H_3O^+(aq) + Cl^-(aq)$$

One mole of dissolved HCl produces two moles of ions: one mole of chloride ion plus one mole of hydronium ion. *All* the dissolved gas reacts, and the HCl is said to be fully ionized (or fully dissociated) in water. Hydrogen chloride may, therefore, be called a *strong* electrolyte even though it is a covalent compound. The aqueous solution of HCl is called hydrochloric acid, and is a major component of gastric juices found in the stomach. HCl is sold commercially as muriatic acid and is used for etching concrete floors before painting, for washing excess mortar from newly laid bricks, and in the maintenance of swimming pools.

A similar reaction of hydrogen gas with fluorine gas produces the covalent compound called hydrogen fluoride, and has the formula HF. HF is a gas that also dissolves in water, but forms only a weakly conducting solution. It reacts as follows:

$$HF(aq) + H_2O(l) \rightleftharpoons H_3O^+(aq) + F^-(aq)$$

The reaction does *not* go to completion, as indicated by the use of the double arrow. Only a very small fraction of the dissolved HF molecules are converted into ions. Dissolving one mole of HF in one liter of water results in a solution containing only 2.6×10^{-2} moles of each ion. This means that only 2.6% of the dissolved HF molecules have reacted with the water to form the two ions. The other 97.4% of the dissolved HF molecules remains in the molecular state. Because HF is found to be only partly ionized in water, it is a weak electrolyte. The aqueous solution of hydrogen fluoride is called hydrofluoric acid. It is one of the few substances that readily attack glass and can be used to etch glass surfaces. Hydrofluoric acid is best stored in plastic bottles.

Ethyl alcohol (C_2H_5OH), also known as ethanol or as grain alcohol, is a more typical covalent compound than the previous examples. Ethyl alcohol is a clear, colorless liquid at room temperature, and is extremely soluble in water. Liquids that are mutually soluble over wide composition ranges are said to be **miscible;** liquids that are not significantly soluble in each other are said to be **immiscible.** Dissolving ethyl alcohol in water produces a nonconducting solution. No true chemical reaction takes place with the water molecules, and the alcohol represents the *non*electrolyte typical of covalent compounds.

The different properties of materials in aqueous solutions are often used to follow the course of a chemical reaction. For example, the so-called acid–base reaction between the dissolved ionic compound $Ba(OH)_2$ (barium hydroxide) and the dissolved covalent compound H_2SO_4 (sulfuric acid) proceeds according to

$$Ba(OH)_2(aq) + H_2SO_4(aq) \rightarrow BaSO_4(s) + 2H_2O(l)$$

Both reactants are strong electrolytes. The barium hydroxide is a water soluble ionic compound and the sulfuric acid is a covalent liquid that reacts in two steps to form three ionic species:

$$H_2SO_4(aq) + H_2O(l) \rightarrow H_3O^+(aq) + HSO_4^-(aq)$$
$$HSO_4^-(aq) + H_2O(l) \rightleftharpoons H_3O^+(aq) + SO_4^{2-}(aq)$$

The first dissociation step goes to completion guaranteeing that *all* the covalent sulfuric acid molecules react to form ions. Sulfuric acid is the acid found in automobile batteries, and is highly corrosive. Neither product of the reaction between barium hydroxide and sulfuric acid results in a conducting solution. Although barium sulfate is ionic, it is very nearly insoluble in water and does not supply significant numbers of mobile ions to the solution.

Assuming that one starts with a solution of barium hydroxide, it will be strongly conductive. As the sulfuric acid solution is slowly added, the four ions react and the number of Ba^{2+} and OH^- ions in the solution decreases; therefore, the conductance of the solution decreases. As the amount of added sulfuric acid reaches the stoichiometric amount, the only substances present are water and the insoluble barium sulfate. The solution would not be expected to conduct electricity at this point. However, as more sulfuric acid is added, the solution no longer encounters any barium hydroxide; since sulfuric acid is a strong electrolyte, the solution conductance again increases. It is exactly at minimal solution conductance that the reaction is complete.

EXPERIMENTAL PROCEDURE

> **CAUTION** WEAR EYE PROTECTION!

PART I Ionic and Covalent Compounds in Solution

A. Concentration Effects

1. Rinse the sample well of the conductivity meter with deionized water and shake dry. If necessary, calibrate the conductivity meter following the directions of your instructor.
2. Add 10.0 mL deionized water to the meter well and obtain a conductivity reading.
3. Add one drop of 0.1 M potassium iodide (KI) solution, gently stir the solution, and again measure the conductivity.
4. Continue the dropwise addition of the KI solution (with stirring), recording each successive measurement, until you have added a total of six drops. You will have to reset the range meter range switch during these measurements.
5. Empty the meter well, rinse with deionized water, and shake dry when you are finished. Explain your observations.

B. Classification of Substances

1. Measure the conductivities of separate 5.0 mL samples of 0.010 M aqueous solutions of each of the following compounds:

HCl	hydrochloric acid	H_2NCONH_2	urea
$C_{12}H_{22}O_{11}$	sucrose	$NaOOCCH_3$	sodium acetate
NaOH	sodium hydroxide	$C_6H_8O_7$	citric acid
$CuSO_4$	copper(II) sulfate	CH_3OH	methanol
$NH_3(aq)$	aqueous ammonia	H_3PO_4	phosphoric acid

2. Between measurements, empty the meter well and rinse the well with the next solution to be examined.
3. Use your conductivity measurements to classify each solute as a *strong, weak,* or *non*electrolyte.

C. Effect of Dissociation

> **CAUTION** The concentrated (glacial) acetic acid used in the next step is corrosive and will burn skin. If skin contact occurs, wash the contacted area with large amounts of water.

1. Rinse and dry the meter well. Add 5.0 mL of pure acetic acid (CH_3COOH) to the well and measure the conductivity of this compound.
2. Measure the conductivity of 0.01 M aqueous acetic acid.
3. Measure the conductivity of 0.01 M hydrochloric acid.
4. Explain your results.

PART II Changes in Solution Conductance During a Reaction

1. Use your small graduated cylinder to add 5.0 mL of deionized water to the sample well of the meter. Add 10 drops 0.05 M H_2SO_4 (sulfuric acid) to the well and stir the solution.

2. Measure and record the conductivity of this dilute sulfuric acid solution. Is this an electrolyte?

3. Add 1 drop 0.05 M $Ba(OH)_2$ (barium hydroxide) solution to the well, stir, and again measure the conductivity. (The barium hydroxide solution might be somewhat cloudy due to a small amount of insoluble barium carbonate, $BaCO_3$. This will cause no harm.)

4. Add a second drop of the $Ba(OH)_2$ solution, stir, and again obtain a conductivity reading. Repeat this procedure until a total of 20 drops $Ba(OH)_2$ solution have been added. Measure and record the conductivity each time.

5. Make a graph plotting solution conductivity on the y-axis and the volume (drops) barium hydroxide added on the x-axis.

6. Explain the changes in the conductivity and the changes in the appearance of the solution. This acid-base reaction can be written as

$$Ba(OH)_2(aq) + H_2SO_4(aq) \rightarrow BaSO_4(s) + 2H_2O(l)$$

Prelaboratory Questions

Solution Conductivity:
Covalent and Ionic Solutes

1. Briefly differentiate between an ionic and a molecular compound.

2. How do you differentiate between a strong electrolyte, a weak electrolyte, and a non-electrolyte?

3. Explain how you can have a solution of a weak electrolyte that is high in concentration.

4. Why do ionic compounds conduct electricity in the molten state, but not in the solid state?

NAME ______________________ SECTION ______________ DATE ______________

Postlaboratory Questions

Solution Conductivity: Covalent and Ionic Solutes

1. For each of the following substances, write the formulas of the principal molecular or ionic species present in an aqueous solution of each substance.
   (a) sodium chloride, $NaCl$

   (b) hydrogen bromide, HBr

   (c) iron(III) sulfate, $Fe_2(SO_4)_3$

   (d) ethanol, CH_3CH_2OH

   (e) glucose, $C_6H_{12}O_6$

   (f) ammonium acetate, NH_4CH_3COO

2. What are spectator ions in chemical reactions?

3. Suppose that Part II of the experiment were carried out with aqueous NaOH (sodium hydroxide) instead of $Ba(OH)_2$ to form soluble Na_2SO_4 along with H_2O as products.
   (a) Write the overall balanced equation.

   (b) Write the net ionic equation.

   (c) How would the graph of conductivity versus volume of aqueous NaOH added differ from the graph you constructed using $Ba(OH)_2$?

4. The electrical conductivity of deionized (or distilled) water is commonly used as an index of its purity. Explain.

5. Pure water in contact with air has a higher conductivity than the same water that has had nitrogen gas bubbled through it. Why?

Report Sheet

Solution Conductivity:
Covalent and Ionic Solutes

PART I   Ionic and Covalent Compounds in Solution

A.   Concentration Effects

Drops of KI soln.	0	1	2	3	4	5	6
Conductivity (μmhos/cm)							

B.   Classification of Substances

Solutions	Conductivity (μmhos/cm)	Strong, weak, or nonelectrolyte
HCl		
sucrose		
NaOH		
$CuSO_4$		
NH_3		
urea		
sodium acetate		
citric acid		
methanol		
phosphoric acid		

C.   Effect of Dissociation

Pure acetic acid   _____ μmhos/cm

0.01 M hydrochloric acid   _____ μmhos/cm

0.01 M acetic acid   _____ μmhos/cm

Explanations:
   Pure acetic acid

0.01 M hydrochloric acid

0.01 M acetic acid

PART II Changes in Solution Conductance During a Reaction

Ba(OH)$_2$ (volume)	Conductivity (μmhos/cm)	Ba(OH)$_2$ (volume)	Conductivity (μmhos/cm)	Ba(OH)$_2$ (volume)	Conductivity (μmhos/cm)
0 drops	_____	7 drops	_____	14 drops	_____
1	_____	8	_____	15	_____
2	_____	9	_____	16	_____
3	_____	10	_____	17	_____
4	_____	11	_____	18	_____
5	_____	12	_____	19	_____
6	_____	13	_____	20	_____

Graph your results and answer the following questions:

1. What is the chemical equation for this reaction?

2. What accounts for the initial decrease in conductivity?

3. What chemical species are present when the conductivity reaches a minimum value?

4. What causes the conductivity to rise again?

Types of Chemical Reactions

OBJECTIVE

To conduct a series of simple experiments, make observations, write balanced equations for the reactions, and classify the reactions as one or more of the types described below.

APPARATUS AND CHEMICALS

test tubes
wood splint
test tube clamp
Bunsen burner
matches
magnesium ribbon
zinc metal
red litmus paper
hydrochloric acid (6 M)
sodium oxide (solid)
manganese dioxide (solid)

hydrogen peroxide (3%)
iron wire
copper sulfate solution (1 M)
sulfuric acid (1 M)
lead nitrate solution (0.1 M)
calcium carbonate (solid)
hydrated copper(II) sulfate (solid)
sodium carbonate solution (0.1 M)
ferrous ammonium sulfate solution (0.1 M)
potassium permanganate solution (0.1 M)

SAFETY CONSIDERATIONS

When using a burner or any open flame in the laboratory, be absolutely sure that loose hair and clothing do not come close to the flame. It is easy to forget this simple rule when concentrating on measurements.

Be sure to wear eye protection. Avoid looking directly at the magnesium ribbon while burning it. Burning magnesium emits brilliant light of sufficient intensity to cause temporary impairment of eyesight if viewed directly.

Objects such as test tubes can be very hot even when they do not look hot. Handle all objects with tongs or test tube holders.

Be sure the gas is turned off when you are through with it because in a closed laboratory a small leak can create an explosive mixture.

Gloves and a laboratory coat will provide additional safety from any corrosive chemical that may splatter on you. Sulfuric acid will burn and dehydrate the skin. Wash the acid off of your skin immediately with much running water. Sulfuric acid will eat through your clothes. Hydrochloric acid can also burn the skin and destroy your clothes.

Potassium permanganate is a strong oxidizing agent. It will permanently bleach any clothing it contacts and will cause holes if not washed off clothing quickly.

FACTS TO KNOW

The elements and compounds may be characterized by the ways in which they react. Most inorganic substances can be classified by five common types of reactions. Those reactions are:

1) **Addition Reactions**

   Reactions where two or more substances combine to give one substance. Note the examples below:

   (1) $S + O_2 \rightarrow SO_2$

   (2) $SO_3 + H_2O \rightarrow H_2SO_4$

2) **Decomposition Reactions**

   A reaction in which one substance breaks down into two or more substances, as the following examples indicate:

   (3) $CaCO_3 \rightarrow CaO + CO_2$

   (4) $2\ NaHCO_3 \rightarrow Na_2CO_3 + H_2O + CO_2$

3) **Oxidation-Reduction Reactions**

   Reactions in which substances experience a change in their oxidation state are oxidation-reduction reactions. Both oxidation and reduction must occur simultaneously. Examples include:

   (5) $2\ Na + Cl_2 \rightarrow 2\ NaCl$

   (6) $Zn + 2\ HCl \rightarrow ZnCl_2 + H_2$

4) **Metathetical (double displacement) Reactions**

   In these reactions, the ions which make up one compound exchange partners with the ions of another compound. The formation of a precipitate (solid) and the evolution of a gas are two signs that a metathetical reaction has occurred. Examples include:

   (7) $AgNO_3 + KBr \rightarrow AgBr$ (a solid) $+ KNO_3$

   (8) $K_2S + 2\ HCl \rightarrow H_2S$ (a gas) $+ 2\ KCl$

5) **Acid-Base Reactions (neutralization)**

   A simple acid-base reaction involves the transfer of a hydrogen ion from the acid to the base. As a result, the acidity of the solution has undergone a change. Examples include:

       acids   bases

   (9) $HCl + NaOH \rightarrow NaCl + H_2O$

   (10) $H_2SO_4 + Ba(OH)_2 \rightarrow BaSO_4 + 2\ H_2O$

Some reactions may be classified by more than one type. For example, reaction 1 above has been classified as an addition reaction. It is also an example of oxidation-reduction. Sulfur and oxygen are both in the zero oxidation state prior to the reaction. After sulfur and oxygen reacted, the sulfur exhibits a $+4$ oxidation state and the oxygen a -2 oxidation state. Also reaction number 6 above is sometimes referred to as a single displacement reaction.

There are a number of observations which give evidence that a chemical reaction has occurred.

1) A change in the acidity of solutions. Litmus paper can be used to detect any change in the acidity of solutions before and after mixing. Acids turn blue litmus paper pink, and bases turn pink litmus blue. Students should test solutions prior to mixing by noticing their effect on litmus. Similarly, test the solution with litmus paper after mixing.

2) Formation of a precipitate (solid). If a precipitate forms when two solutions are mixed, a reaction has occurred.

3) Evolution of a gas. The formation of a gas is evidence that a reaction has occurred. The evolution of a gas can be detected by its color, odor, acidity, and/or by its combustibility.

4) Color change. Brightly colored solids often will undergo a change in color upon heating. This color change indicates that the solid has undergone decomposition.

5) Observable temperature change. All reactions are accompanied by energy changes of some sort. These may include sound (ex. an explosion), light (a fire), electric current (battery discharging), and heat. Many reactions give off a combination of forms of energy (an explo sion produces light, heat, and sound). Sometimes the only observable change accompanying a reaction is the absorption or release of energy. For example, when a solution of aqueous HCl is added to a solution of aqueous NaOH to form an aqueous solution of NaCl (and a little more water), it *looks like* water being added to water making more water, except that it gets hot!

PROCEDURE

Below are a series of reactions to be conducted. Follow the directions for each reaction and use the data sheet to provide the following:

    (a) your observations   (b) the reaction type   (c) a balanced equation

(1) Demonstration by instructor: Secure a piece of magnesium ribbon about 3 inches long, hold one end with tongs, and ignite one end of it with a match. *CAUTION:* Look at this reaction out of the side of your eyes rather than looking directly at the hot spot in the center of the flame.

(2) Place a few small pieces of zinc metal in a clean test tube and add a few drops of dilute hydrochloric acid (HCl).

(3) Add 2 mL of 3% H_2O_2 to a small test tube. Use a spatula to add a small amount of MnO_2 (0.1 g). Hold a glowing splint in the end of the test tube to test whether the gas given off supports combustion. MnO_2 is a catalyst in this reaction. Explain this in the observations section.

(4) Place a few pieces of iron wire in a test tube containing about 5 mL of copper sulfate ($CuSO_4$) solution. Allow several minutes for a reaction to occur.

(5) Add a few drops of 1 M sulfuric acid (H_2SO_4) solution to a test tube containing about 2 mL of lead nitrate ($Pb(NO_3)_2$) solution.

(6) Place a small amount of calcium carbonate ($CaCO_3$) solid in a clean, dry test tube and slowly add dilute hydrochloric acid dropwise.

(7) Place about 1 g of solid copper sulfate hydrate ($CuSO_4 \cdot 5H_2O$) in a clean, dry test tube and heat for several minutes.

(8) Test the acidity of tap water using red litmus paper. Dissolve about 0.1 g of sodium oxide (Na2O) solid in the water and repeat the test with red litmus paper. *red → Blue = Change*
    NaOH

(9) Place about 3 mL of a solution of ferrous ammonium sulfate ($Fe(NH_4)_2(SO_4)_2$) in a test tube. Add dropwise a solution of potassium permanganate ($KMnO_4$).

(10) Place about 3 mL of a solution of Na_2CO_3 in a clean test tube and test its acidity with a piece of red litmus. Add slowly about 20 drops of dilute hydrochloric acid and test the acidity of this solution with red litmus paper.

PRE-LAB QUESTIONS

1. What precaution must be taken when burning magnesium ribbon is observed?

    _____

2. State briefly what should be done if sulfuric acid is spilled on the skin.

    _____

3. List two observations which you can make which indicate that a chemical reaction has occurred.

    1. _____

    2. _____

4. State the color which litmus paper will change to in:

    2. acid solution _____

    3. basic solution _____

TYPES OF CHEMICAL REACTIONS

Observations	Reaction Type	Complete and Balance*
(1)		$2\ Mg + O_2 \rightarrow$
(2)		$Zn + 2\ HCl\ (aq) \rightarrow$
(3)		$2\ H_2O_2\ (aq) \overset{MnO_2}{\rightarrow}$
(4)		$Fe + CuSO_4\ (aq) \rightarrow$
(5)		$Pb(NO_3)_2\ (aq) + H_2SO_4\ (aq) \rightarrow$
(6)		$CaCO_3\ (s) + 2\ HCl\ (aq) \rightarrow$
(7)		$CuSO_4 \cdot 5H_2O_{(s)} \overset{\Delta}{\rightarrow}$
(8)		$Na_2O_{(s)} + H_2O \rightarrow$
(9)		$FeSO_4\ (aq) + KMnO_4\ (aq) \rightarrow$
(10)		$Na_2CO_3\ (aq) + 2\ HCl\ (aq) \rightarrow$

* An aqueous (water) solution is represented by the symbol (aq).

POST-LAB QUESTIONS

1. Manganese dioxide (MnO_2) was added to the test tube containing hydrogen peroxide (H_2O_2). Why was this added? _____

   What can the manganese dioxide be called when it is used for this purpose?

   _____

2. What color did the litmus paper turn to when you tested tap water? _____
   Make a guess as to why tap water gave this reaction. _____

   _____

3. Write the name and formula for the chemical substance which is always produced in a neutralization reaction.

   1. name _____

   2. formula _____

Chemical Equations: A Study Assignment

Performance Goal

Given information from which you can write the formulas for all reactants and all products for each of the following types of reactions, write the balanced chemical equation for the reactions:

Combination
Decomposition
Complete oxidation or burning of organic compounds
Ion combination, forming a precipitate or molecular product
Oxidation–reduction ("single replacement" equations only)
Other reactions in which reactants and products are identified

CHEMICAL OVERVIEW

A chemist uses a chemical equation to describe a chemical change. The general form of a chemical equation is

$$\text{Reactant 1} + \text{Reactant 2} + \ldots \rightarrow \text{Product 1} + \text{Product 2} + \ldots$$

The substances that enter into the reaction are called **reactants.** They are identified by their chemical formulas, written on the left side of the equation, and separated from each other by plus signs. The formulas of the new substances produced in the reaction, called **products,** are written on the right side, again separated by plus signs. The two sides of the equation are separated by an arrow pointing from the reactants to the products, indicating that the reactants are changed into the products. In reading a chemical equation, or expressing it in words, the arrow is frequently read as "yields," "produces," or "forms"; any other term that suggests the creation of a substance not originally present is equally satisfactory.

Symbols are frequently added to chemical equations to indicate the conditions under which the reaction occurs. The symbols (s), (ℓ), or (g) immediately after the formula of a substance indicate that the substance is in the solid, liquid, or gaseous state, respectively. A substance that is in aqueous (water) solution may have (aq) after its formula. An arrow pointing up after a formula indicates a gaseous product that escapes to the atmosphere; an arrow pointing down identifies a product that is precipitated, or formed into a solid, from a solution. Sometimes the arrow between reactants and products is lengthened, and words, formulas, temperatures, or other symbols are written above (or above and below) the arrow to indicate reaction conditions or other substances in the reaction vessel. None of these supplementary items will be used in this exercise; however, if your instructor requests that you use them, you should, of course, follow his or her directions.

A chemical equation does two things. First, it tells you what substances are involved in a chemical change. To do this accurately, it is essential that the substances be represented by their correct chemical formulas. It is assumed in this exercise that, given the name of a chemical, you are able to write its formula. Second, an equation has quantitative significance. It obeys the law of conservation of mass, which indicates that the total mass of all the reactants is equal to the total mass of all the products in an ordinary chemical change. In order for this to be true, the equation must have equal numbers of atoms of each individual element on the two sides of the equation. The equation is then said to be **balanced.**

These two characteristics of an equation lead to a simple two-step procedure by which an equation may be written:

1. Write the correct chemical formula for each reactant on the left and each product on the right.
2. *Using coefficients only,* balance the number of atoms of each element on each side of the equation. If no coefficient is written, its value is assumed to be one (1).

It is impossible to overemphasize the importance of following these two steps literally, and keeping them independent. In Step 1, write the correct formulas without concern about where the atoms come from, or how many atoms of an element may be present in some species on the other side of the equation. In Step 2, be sure that you balance the atoms of each element by placing whole-number coefficients in front of chemical formulas, and by no other means. Specifically,

DO NOT   change a correct chemical formula in order to balance an element;
DO NOT   add some real or imaginary chemical species to either side to make an element balance.

Quite often the word description of a chemical reaction will not identify all of the species that must be included in the equation. If you are familiar with the kinds of reactions described in the performance goal, you will be able to identify the substances not mentioned. The reaction types will be discussed as they are encountered.

EXAMPLES

The following examples are in the form of a program in which you learn by answering a series of questions. Obtain an opaque shield (a piece of cardboard, or a folded piece of paper you cannot see through) that is wide enough to cover this page. In each example place the shield on the book page so it covers everything beneath the first dotted line that runs across the page. Read to that point, and write in the space provided whatever is asked. Then lower the shield to the next dotted line. The material exposed will begin with the correct response to the question you have just answered. Compare this answer to yours, looking back to correct any misunderstanding if the two are different. When you fully understand the first step, read to the next dotted line and proceed as before.

A. Combination Reactions. A combination reaction occurs when two or more substances combine to form a single product. The reactants may be elements or compounds, perhaps one or more of each. Quite often the description of the reaction will give the chemical name of the product only. For example, the equation for the reaction in which sodium chloride is formed from its elements is $2\,Na + Cl_2 \rightarrow 2\,NaCl$. An example of a combination reaction between compounds is $CaO + H_2O \rightarrow Ca(OH)_2$.

Example 1

Write the equation showing how magnesium oxide is formed from its elements.

". . . magnesium oxide is formed . . ." indicates that magnesium oxide is the product of the reaction, so its formula will appear on the right side of the equation. ". . . from its elements" identifies magnesium and oxygen as the reactants whose formulas will be written to the left of the arrow. Complete Step 1 of the procedure by writing the unbalanced equation.

· ·

1a. $Mg + O_2 \rightarrow MgO$

Remember, oxygen is a diatomic element; its correct formula is therefore O_2 and not simply O.

Step 2 calls for you to balance the atoms of each element on the two sides of the equation. As it stands, there is one magnesium atom on each side; magnesium is in balance. The left side of the equation has two atoms of oxygen, and the right side only one. What must you do to balance oxygen? Remember, there is only one way to do it, and watch out for the DON'Ts listed earlier. Balance the oxygen.

$$Mg + O_2 \rightarrow MgO$$

. . . .

1b. $Mg + O_2 \rightarrow 2\,MgO$

Remember, your only way to balance atoms of an element in Step 2 is to use coefficients in front of substances in the unbalanced equation. Some common WRONG responses to the above — and what is wrong with them — are:

$Mg + O_2 \rightarrow MgO + O$	There are no oxygen atoms in the reaction. This violates the second DON'T.
$Mg + O_2 \rightarrow MgO_2$	MgO_2 happens to be a real substance, but it is *not* the product of this reaction. This violates the first DON'T.
$Mg + O_2 \rightarrow Mg\,2\,O$	Mg 2 O is not a chemical formula. Coefficients are placed in front of a formula, not in the middle, and they affect the entire formula.

The last of the three wrong balancing methods points out that in balancing oxygen we have *un*balanced magnesium. There is now one magnesium atom on the left and two on the right. Correct this now.

. . . .

1c. $2\,Mg + O_2 \rightarrow 2\,MgO$

There is another way you might have balanced $Mg + O_2 \rightarrow MgO$. You could have introduced the fractional coefficient 1/2 in front of oxygen: $Mg + 1/2\,O_2 \rightarrow MgO$. While fractional coefficients are technically correct, they are not commonly used, and should not be used in this exercise. They may be used as a means to the final equation, however. If you do choose to balance the equation with a fractional coefficient, as above, you can then multiply the entire equation by 2 (doubling *each* coefficient), giving $2\,Mg + O_2 \rightarrow 2\,MgO$. Incidentally, equations should be written with the *smallest* whole-number coefficients. If, in your balancing procedure, you happened to arrive at $4\,Mg + 2\,O_2 \rightarrow 4\,MgO$, you could divide the entire equation — each coefficient — by 2 to get the desired result.

Example 2

Write the equation for the formation of iron(III) oxide from its elements.

Complete the first step by writing the formulas of the reactants on the left and the formula of the product on the right.

. . . .

2a. $Fe + O_2 \rightarrow Fe_2O_3$

Start with the iron; balance it first and leave oxygen unbalanced.

. . . .

2b. $2 Fe + \quad O_2 \rightarrow \quad Fe_2O_3$

There are two thought processes by which balancing may be completed, both leading to the same result. Both will be discussed — after you have balanced the rest of the equation yourself.

. . . .

2c. $4 Fe + 3 O_2 \rightarrow 2 Fe_2O_3$

Oxygen atoms come two to the package in O_2 molecules, and three to the package in Fe_2O_3 units. Six atoms — 2 times 3 — is the smallest number of atoms by which a 3-and-2 combination can be equalized. If you take 3 packages of 2 each, you will have the same number as 2 packages of 3 each. This fixes the coefficients of O_2 and Fe_2O_3. The coefficient of iron is adjusted to correspond with the iron atoms in 2 Fe_2O_3.

A second way of reaching the final equation is to select the fractional coefficient of O_2 that will give the proper number of oxygen atoms to balance the three on the right side of $2 Fe + O_2 \rightarrow Fe_2O_3$. With three oxygens on the right, we need three on the left, where they come two to a package in O_2. We therefore need $1\frac{1}{2}$ packages, or 3/2, yielding $2 Fe + 3/2 O_2 \rightarrow Fe_2O_3$. This balanced equation can be cleared of fractions by multiplying all coefficients by 2, giving $4 Fe + 3 O_2 \rightarrow 2 Fe_2O_3$.

It is worthwhile to become familiar with both methods. The 3-and-2 combination appears frequently enough to justify the routine 2-of-3 and 3-of-2 thought process. It is convenient to realize that if you need X atoms of oxygen from O_2 molecules, the number of molecules required is $X/2$. Doubling the equation yields whole-number coefficients.

B. Decomposition Reactions. The chemical change in which a single reactant decomposes into two or more products is a decomposition reaction. This is just the opposite of a combination reaction; indeed, many combination reactions can be reversed, as $2 NaCl \rightarrow 2 Na + Cl_2$. The reaction $2 Al(OH)_3 \rightarrow Al_2O_3 + 3 H_2O$ illustrates a decomposition of a compound into two simpler compounds. Another type of decomposition reaction occurs when hydrates (compounds containing water of hydration) are heated. $Na_2CO_3 \cdot 10H_2O \xrightarrow{\Delta} Na_2CO_3 + 10 H_2O$ illustrates such a reaction, where Δ written over the arrow generally means "applying heat."

Example 3

Calcium carbonate is decomposed into calcium oxide and carbon dioxide by heat. Write the equation.

The first step is to write the formulas of reactants and products in their proper places. Proceed that far.

. . . .

3a. $CaCO_3 \rightarrow \quad CaO + \quad CO_2$

Now Step 2: balance the atoms of each element on the two sides of the equation.

3b. $CaCO_3 \rightarrow CaO + CO_2$

Sometimes balancing an equation is easy — particularly when all coefficients are 1!

C. Complete Oxidation or Burning of Organic Compounds.   Other than the oxides of carbon, carbonates, and a few other substances, the compounds of carbon are classified as **organic compounds.** Hydrogen is almost always present in an organic compound, and oxygen is a third very common element. When compounds containing carbon and hydrogen, or carbon, hydrogen, and oxygen, react *completely* with an excess of oxygen, the products are always carbon dioxide and water. Such a reaction may occur with the oxygen in the air, giving heat and light, in which case the process is called **burning;** and it may occur in living organisms, again giving off heat and other forms of energy, in which case it is referred to as **oxidation.** The description of such a reaction may be very brief: Compound X is completely oxidized, or Compound Y is burned in air. In both reactions you must recognize oxygen as an unnamed reactant to be included in the equation, and write the formulas of carbon dioxide and water as the products. $2\ C_6H_{14} + 19\ O_2 \rightarrow 12\ CO_2 + 14\ H_2O$ is an example of a burning reaction. Because organic compounds are frequently quite large, equations may have large coefficients; but don't let that bother you, as they are reached by the same method outlined above.

Example 4

Write the equation for the complete oxidation of methyl ethyl ketone, $CH_3COC_2H_5$.

Methyl ethyl ketone has been chosen for this example because its equation includes all the little things you must look out for in writing oxidation equations. First, notice that organic chemists sometimes write formulas in ways that seem strange to the beginning student. This is because the sequences of elements and certain combinations in the formula suggest how atoms are arranged in the molecule and identify the kind of compound it is. Secondly, you must be sure to count *all* the atoms of a given element in a molecular formula when balancing, such as 4 carbon atoms, 8 hydrogen atoms, and 1 oxygen atom in a molecule of $CH_3COC_2H_5$. A third point will show up later. Right now, complete Step 1 by writing the formulas of reactants and products in their proper places in an unbalanced equation.

4a. $CH_3COC_2H_5 + \quad O_2 \rightarrow \quad CO_2 + \quad H_2O$

Always remember that, although it is unnamed in the statement of the reaction, oxygen is a second reactant and the products are carbon dioxide and water.

To begin Step 2, you balance both carbon and hydrogen. With the warning already given, add those coefficients to the equation.

4b. $CH_3COC_2H_5 + \quad O_2 \rightarrow \quad 4\ CO_2 + \quad 4\ H_2O$

With carbon and hydrogen balanced, and oxygen in its elemental form on the left, oxygen can be balanced simply by placing in front of oxygen the coefficient that does the job. Sounds simple, but be careful . . .

4c. $2 CH_3COC_2H_5 + 11 O_2 \rightarrow 8 CO_2 + 8 H_2O$

Starting from $CH_3COC_2H_5 + O_2 \rightarrow 4 CO_2 + 4 H_2O$, you count 12 oxygen atoms on the right side of the equation. On the left, *one of the required 12 oxygen atoms comes from the reactant,* and the remaining *eleven* come from O_2. This is the third thing you must look out for in balancing oxidation equations, being sure not to overlook oxygen present in the compound being oxidized. With 11 oxygen atoms to come from O_2, you can balance the equation with a fractional coefficient: $CH_3COC_2H_5 + 11/2 O_2 \rightarrow 4 CO_2 + 4 H_2O$. Doubling the entire equation gives whole-number coefficients, as required.

D. Oxidation–Reduction Reactions.   The words **oxidize** and **oxidation** have meaning in chemistry other than "reaction with oxygen," as suggested in the foregoing section. In its broader meaning, oxidation means loss of electrons. If one reactant loses electrons, another reactant must gain those electrons. The process of gaining electrons is called **reduction.** A reaction in which oxidation and reduction occur — and they must always occur simultaneously — is called an **oxidation–reduction reaction,** frequently shortened to "redox" reaction.

In this exercise we will be concerned with only one kind of redox reaction. The equation has the appearance of an element reacting with a compound in such a manner that the element replaces one of the elements in the compound. $Zn + Cu(NO_3)_2 \rightarrow Cu + Zn(NO_3)_2$ is such a reaction. It appears as if elemental zinc has replaced copper from $Cu(NO_3)_2$. This kind of equation is frequently called a **single replacement equation.** Given an element and an ionic compound as reactants, you should recognize the possibility of a redox reaction and be able to write the single replacement equation for that reaction. Whether or not the reaction actually occurs requires laboratory confirmation, of course.

Example 5

Gaseous hydrogen is released when zinc reacts with hydrochloric acid. Write the equation for the reaction.

The reactants and one of the products are identified. As you write the unbalanced equation (Step 1) for these three species, see if you can recognize the single replacement character of that equation and then figure out the formula of the second product.

5a. $Zn + \quad HCl \rightarrow \quad H_2 + \quad ZnCl_2$

In the reaction zinc is releasing, or replacing, hydrogen in HCl. The second product is therefore zinc chloride. Balancing the equation is straightforward . . .

5b. $Zn + 2 HCl \rightarrow H_2 + ZnCl_2$

Example 6

Write the equation for the reaction between aluminum and nickel nitrate.

This time you are given only the names of two reactants. Write their formulas on the left side of the arrow, leaving the product side blank.

6a.   Al + Ni(NO$_3$)$_2$ →

Here's where your skill in recognizing the possibility of a redox reaction comes into play. What possible products could come from these reactants? There is no indication that the nitrate ion decomposes. Ions of aluminum and nickel are both positively charged, so there is no way they could form a compound. The nitrate ion is negatively charged, so it could form a compound with an aluminum ion. It all points to a single replacement equation in which aluminum bumps nickel out of the compound. Complete Step 1 by writing the formulas of the products on the right side of the equation.

6b.   Al +   Ni(NO$_3$)$_2$ →   Ni +   Al(NO$_3$)$_3$

This example gives us an opportunity to introduce an important technique in balancing equations. A quick glance shows that aluminum and nickel are balanced, but nitrogen and oxygen are not. You could balance them individually, but there is an easier way. It was noted above that the *nitrate ion* does not decompose in the reaction; in other words, the nitrate ion is the same on the product side of the equation as it is on the reactant side. Any time a polyatomic (many atom) ion is unchanged in a chemical reaction, that ion may be balanced *as a unit* in the equation. In other words, your thought process should be, "There are two nitrate ions on the left, and three nitrate ions on the right. How do I balance them?" How *do* you balance a 3-and-2 combination? You already know that, so go ahead. While you're at it, be sure to do whatever is necessary to keep the aluminum and nickel in balance.

6c.   2 Al + 3 Ni(NO$_3$)$_2$ → 3 Ni + 2 Al(NO$_3$)$_3$

You need 3 nickel nitrate units, where nitrate ions appear in packages of two, to balance 2 aluminum nitrate units, where the nitrate ions appear in packages of three, giving 6 nitrate ions on each side of the equation. The coefficients for the metals complete the equation.

E.   Ion Combination Reactions.   As the name suggests, ion combination reactions involve the combination of ions from different sources to form a new product. If two ions are to combine, one must have a positive charge and the other must have a negative charge. The combination of a lead ion from lead(II) nitrate and a chloride ion from sodium chloride to form lead(II) chloride is a good example: Pb(NO$_3$)$_2$ + 2 NaCl → PbCl$_2$ + 2 NaNO$_3$. If you look at the equation, it appears as if the positive and negative ions in the two reactants have simply "changed partners" in the products; the positive ion of the first reactant has joined up with the negative ion of the second reactant, and the negative ion of the first has combined with the positive ion of the second. This kind of equation is called a **double displacement equation.** Whenever you see an equation with two ionized reactants, you can make an intelligent prediction that the products will be derived from an exchange of ions, and write their formulas accordingly.

Most ion combination reactions occur in water solution. One of the driving forces for these reactions is the formation of an insoluble ionic solid, called a **precipitate.** In the example above, lead(II) chloride is insoluble in water, so it precipitates as the ions combine with each other.

The other driving force that brings ions together is the formation of a molecular product, in which a covalent (shared electron pair) bond forms between the reacting ions. The most common molecular product is water, as in HCl + KOH → KCl + H$_2$O. This kind of reaction, in which an acid reacts with a base, is called a **neutralization reaction.** The ionic product formed (KCl, in this example) is classified as a **salt.**

Example 7

Write the equation for the precipitation reaction that occurs when sodium hydroxide is added to a solution of copper(II) nitrate.

You are given the reactants. Write their formulas to the left of the arrow, leaving the right side blank.

. . . .

7a. $NaOH + Cu(NO_3)_2 \rightarrow$

Once the reactant formulas are written, it is easier to see the new combinations of ions that are possible. Write the formulas of the product species on the right.

. . . .

7b. $NaOH + \quad Cu(NO_3)_2 \rightarrow \quad NaNO_3 + \quad Cu(OH)_2$

The positively charged sodium ion from the first reactant is shown as combined with the negatively charged nitrate ion from the second reactant, and the cation from the second combines with the anion from the first. The ions have "changed partners."

In balancing the equation, remember what you have learned about balancing as units any polyatomic ions that are unchanged in the reaction. In this case it is a lot easier than balancing oxygen by itself, appearing, as it does, in all four compounds. Go ahead — complete the equation.

. . . .

7c. $2 NaOH + Cu(NO_3)_2 \rightarrow 2 NaNO_3 + Cu(OH)_2$

In addition to the sodium and copper being balanced, the equation shows two hydroxide ions and two nitrate ions on each side.

Example 8

Write the equation for the neutralization of sulfuric acid by lithium hydroxide.

The procedure in this example is the same as in the last. This time complete Step 1, writing formulas of both reactants and products in their proper places.

. . . .

8a. $H_2SO_4 + \quad LiOH \rightarrow \quad Li_2SO_4 + \quad H_2O$

Balancing this equation is easy enough, but the thought processes are important. See if you can think it through in terms of hydrogen and hydroxide ions.

. . . .

8b. $H_2SO_4 + 2 LiOH \rightarrow Li_2SO_4 + 2 H_2O$

Lithium and the sulfate ions balance in the usual manner. The two hydrogens in H_2SO_4 are balanced by the first hydrogen (underlined) in 2 $\underline{H}OH$ (H_2O) molecules. The two hydroxide ions in 2 LiOH are balanced by the OH parts of 2 $H\underline{OH}$ molecules.

Water is not the only molecular product that may be formed, as the following example illustrates.

Example 9

Write the equation for the reaction between nitric acid and sodium acetate, $NaC_2H_3O_2$.

First the formulas of the reactants only . . .

. . . .

9a. $HNO_3 + NaC_2H_3O_2 \rightarrow$

The formula of sodium acetate was given to you partly because the acetate ion is probably not familiar to you, but more importantly because we didn't want you to look it up. Instead, you should figure out what the charge on the ion is from the formula of sodium acetate. Then figure out how many hydrogen ions will combine with how many acetate ions to form the molecular product, acetic acid. Write that formula, as well as the formula of the salt produced in the reaction, on the right side of the equation. Balance the equation, too.

. . . .

9b. $HNO_3 + NaC_2H_3O_2 \rightarrow HC_2H_3O_2 + NaNO_3$

If there is one Na^+ ion in a formula unit of $NaC_2H_3O_2$, the acetate ion must consist of everything else in the compound, with a negative charge equal to the positive charge of the sodium ion: $C_2H_3O_2^-$. The 1− charge of the acetate ion requires the 1+ charge of a hydrogen ion, H^+, to form a neutral molecule, so the formula of acetic acid must be $HC_2H_3O_2$. The equation is balanced with all coefficients equal to 1.

F. Other Reactions in Which Reactants and Products Are Identified.   Many kinds of chemical reactions do not fit into any of the classifications we have considered. Therefore, you cannot be expected to predict what substances might be formed in such reactions, nor to predict the formulas of these products. If you are given the names and/or formulas of all species in an unclassified reaction, however, you should be able to write the equation.

Example 10

Carbon dioxide and water are two of the three products of the reaction between magnesium carbonate and hydrochloric acid. Write the equation.

You have two reactants and two out of three products identified. See if you can write the formula of the third product, too, as you complete Step 1 of the procedure. If you get that far, balancing is easy. Go all the way.

. . . .

10a. $MgCO_3 + 2\ HCl \rightarrow MgCl_2 + CO_2 + H_2O$

The reactant formulas suggest a typical double displacement equation, which probably describes accurately what first occurs in the reaction. The H_2CO_3 you would expect as a product is unstable, however, and decomposes into CO_2 and H_2O. Even without this reasoning, you could conclude that $MgCl_2$ is the unnamed product. The only reacting ions not accounted for in the identified products, CO_2 and H_2O, are Mg^{2+} and Cl^-. It is logical that $MgCl_2$ be the third product.

Report Sheet

EQUATION-WRITING EXERCISE

Write the chemical equation for each reaction described below.

A) Combination Reactions

    1) Diphosphorus trioxide is formed by direct combination of its elements.

    2) Ammonia and sulfuric acid combine to form ammonium sulfate.

B) Decomposition Reactions

    3) Ammonium nitrite decomposes into nitrogen and water.

    4) When heated, potassium chlorate decomposes into oxygen and potassium chloride.

C) Complete Oxidation or Burning of Organic Compounds

    5) Propane, C_3H_8, burns in air.

    6) Acetaldehyde, CH_3CHO, is completely oxidized.

D) Oxidation – Reduction Reactions

7) Hydrogen is released when aluminum reacts with hydrochloric acid.

8) Magnesium reacts with silver nitrate solution.

E) Ion Combination Reactions

9) Barium carbonate precipitates from the reaction of barium chloride and sodium carbonate solutions.

10) Sulfuric acid neutralizes calcium hydroxide.

11) Sodium iodate and silver nitrate solutions are combined.

12) Potassium fluoride reacts with hydrobromic acid.

13) Zinc hydroxide reacts with hydrochloric acid.

Report Sheet

F) Other Reactions

14) Copper(II) chloride and water result from the reaction of copper(II) oxide and hydrochloric acid.

15) Carbon dioxide and water are two of the three products from the reaction of sulfuric acid with sodium hydrogen carbonate.

G) Mixed Reactions

16) Hydrobromic acid reacts with potassium hydroxide.

17) Aluminum reacts with phosphoric acid.

18) Silver nitrate reacts with hydrosulfuric acid.

19) Phosphorus triiodide is formed from its elements.

20) Iron(II) chloride reacts with sodium phosphate.

21) Sugar, $C_{12}H_{22}O_{11}$, is burned in air.

22) Sugar, $C_{12}H_{22}O_{11}$, breaks down to carbon and water when heated.

23) Lithium hydroxide solution comes from the reaction of lithium oxide and water.

24) Magnesium sulfate reacts with sodium hydroxide.

25) Chlorine reacts with a solution of sodium iodide.

26) Nickel hydroxide reacts with sulfuric acid.

Report Sheet

27) Barium peroxide, BaO_2, decomposes into oxygen and barium oxide.

28) Ammonia is formed from its elements.

29) Butyl alcohol, C_4H_9OH, is oxidized completely.

30) Water is driven from copper sulfate pentahydrate, $CuSO_4 \cdot 5\ H_2O$, with heat.

31) Magnesium nitride is formed by its elements.

32) Sulfuric acid reacts with potassium nitrite.

Advance Study Assignment

1) What is the first step in writing a chemical equation?

2) What two things must *not* be done when balancing an equation?

3) What reactant is frequently not named in a burning reaction? What are the products of all complete oxidations of compounds consisting of carbon, hydrogen, and possibly oxygen?

4) Name two kinds of chemical reactions that are described by double displacement equations.

5) What term is used to describe the equation that is written for a redox reaction in which an element appears to take the place of another element in a compound?

Qualitative Analysis of Some Common Ions

Performance Goals

7–1 Conduct tests to confirm the presence of known ions in a solution.

7–2 Analyze an unknown solution for certain ions.

CHEMICAL OVERVIEW

When we analyze an unknown solution, two questions come to mind: (a) what ions are present in the solution, and (b) what is their concentration? The first question can be answered by performing a **qualitative analysis,** and the second by a **quantitative analysis.** These two broad categories are known collectively as **analytical chemistry.** In this experiment, you will perform a qualitative analysis.

The general approach to finding out what ions are in a solution is to test for the presence of each possible component by adding a reagent that will cause that component, if present, to react in a certain way. This method involves a series of tests, one for each component, carried out on separate samples of solution. Difficulty sometimes arises, particularly in complex mixtures, because one of the species may interfere with the analytical test for another. Although interferences are common, many ions in mixtures can usually be identified by simple tests.

In this experiment, you will analyze an unknown mixture that may contain one or more of the following ions in solution:

$$CO_3^{2-} \quad Cl^- \quad SCN^- \quad SO_4^{2-}$$
$$PO_4^{3-} \quad Cu^{2+} \quad Al^{3+} \quad Fe^{3+}$$

First, you will perform the various tests designed to detect the presence of individual ions. Once you have observed these specific reactions, you will obtain the unknown solution from your instructor. Then, taking small portions of this solution, you will run each reaction again to determine which ions are present and which are absent.

This experiment is designed to test the behavior of only a few ions. More complex schemes are used for a more complete qualitative analysis.

SAFETY PRECAUTIONS AND DISPOSAL METHODS

In some tests you will be required to use fairly concentrated acids and bases. When in contact with skin, most of these chemicals cause severe burns if not removed promptly. Wear goggles when working with any of the reagents required in this experiment.

Discard solutions containing heavy metal precipitates in the container provided.

PROCEDURE

A boiling water bath is required for some of the tests you are to perform. Pour about 100 mL of deionized water into a 150-mL beaker and heat it to boiling. Maintain it at that temperature throughout the experiment, replenishing the water from time to time as it becomes necessary.

1. TEST FOR THE CARBONATE ION, CO_3^{2-}

Cautiously add about 10 drops of 1 M HCl to 10 drops of 1 M Na_2CO_3 in a small-size test tube. Bubbles of a colorless and odorless gas, carbon dioxide, usually appear immediately in the presence of the carbonate ion. If the bubbles are not readily apparent, warm the solution in the hot-water bath and stir.

2. TEST FOR THE SULFATE ION, SO_4^{2-}

Cautiously add about 10 drops of 1 M HCl to 10 drops of 0.5 M Na_2SO_4. Then add 3 to 4 drops of 1 M $BaCl_2$. A white, powdery precipitate of $BaSO_4$ indicates the presence of SO_4^{2-} ions in the sample.

3. TEST FOR PHOSPHATE ION, PO_4^{3-}

Add 1 M HNO_3 to 10 drops of 0.5 M Na_3PO_4 until the solution is acidic. (Test by dipping a stirring rod into the solution and touching the wet rod to a strip of blue litmus paper. The solution is acidic if the color changes to red.) Then add 5 drops of 0.5 M $(NH_4)_2MoO_4$ and heat the test tube in a hot-water bath. A powdery, light yellow precipitate indicates the presence of PO_4^{3-} ions.

> **Caution: The molybdate solution is yellow. Be sure you see a precipitate before concluding that PO432 is present.**

4. TEST FOR THIOCYANATE ION, SCN^-

Add 10 drops of 3 M $HC_2H_3O_2$ to about 10 drops of 0.5 M KSCN and stir with a glass rod. Add 1 or 2 drops of 0.1 M $Fe(NO_3)_3$. A **deep** red color formation is proof of the presence of SCN^- ions.

5. TEST FOR CHLORIDE ION, Cl^-

   A)   Add 1 mL of 1 M HNO_3 to about 1 mL of 0.5 M NaCl. Add 2 or 3 drops of 0.1 M $AgNO_3$. A white precipitate of AgCl confirms the presence of chloride ion.

   B)   If thiocyanate ion is present, it will interfere with this test, since it also forms a white precipitate with $AgNO_3$. If the sample contains SCN^- ion, put 10 drops of the solution in a medium-size test tube and add 10 drops of 1 M HNO_3. Boil the solution gently until the volume is reduced to half. This procedure will oxidize the thiocyanate and remove the interference. Then perform the chloride ion test as previously explained.

6. TEST FOR ALUMINUM ION, Al^{3+}

Add 1 M NH_3 dropwise to about 10 drops of 0.5 M $AlCl_3$ until the solution is basic (red litmus turns blue). A white, gelatinous precipitate, $Al(OH)_3$, will form. Add 3 M $HC_2H_3O_2$ dropwise until the solid dissolves. Stir and add 2 drops of cathecol violet reagent. A blue solution indicates the presence of Al^{3+} ions.

7. TEST FOR THE COPPER(II) ION, Cu^{2+}

Add concentrated ammonia drop by drop to about 10 drops of 0.5 M $CuSO_4$. The development of a dark blue color is proof of the presence of copper(II) ion.

8. TEST FOR THE IRON(III) ION, Fe^{3+}

This test is essentially the same as the test used for the thiocyanate, SCN^-, ion. To about 10 drops of 0.1 M $Fe(NO_3)_3$ add 3 or 4 drops of 0.5 M KSCN. A **deep** red color will appear if Fe^{3+} ions are present.

9. ANALYSIS OF AN UNKNOWN

When you have completed all of the tests, obtain an unknown from the instructor. Analyze it by using 10 drop portions of the unknown and then applying the tests to separate portions. The unknown will contain three to five of the ions on the list, so your test for a given ion may be affected by the presence of others. If a test does not go quite as expected, try to figure out why the sample may have behaved as it did. When you think you have analyzed your unknown properly, you may, if you wish, make a "known" that has the same ions you have found and test it to see if it has the properties of the unknown.

Work Page

Ions Tested	Observations (Known)	Unknown	
		Yes	No
CO_3^{2-}			
SO_4^{2-}			
PO_4^{3-}			
SCN^-			
Cl^-			
Al^{3+}			
Cu^{2+}			
Fe^{3+}			

Unknown Number _____ .   Ions present _____

Report Sheet

Ions Tested	Observations (Known)	Unknown	
		Yes	No
CO_3^{2-}			
SO_4^{2-}			
PO_4^{3-}			
SCN^-			
Cl^-			
Al^{3+}			
Cu^{2+}			
Fe^{3+}			

Unknown Number _____ . Ions present _____

Advance Study Assignment

1) An unknown that might contain any of the eight ions studied in this experiment (but no other ions) has the following properties:

   a. On addition of 1 M HCl, bubbles form.
   b. When 0.1 M $BaCl_2$ is added to the acidified unknown, a white precipitate results.
   c. When 0.1 M $AgNO_3$ is added to the unknown, a clear solution results.

On the basis of the preceding information, classify each of the following ions as present (P), absent (A), or undetermined (U) by the tests described:

CO_3^{2-} _____; SO_4^{2-} _____; PO_4^{3-} _____; SCN^- _____;

Cl^- _____; Al^{3+} _____; Cu^{2+} _____; Fe^{3+} _____.

OPTIONAL ASSIGNMENT

Write net ionic equations for the reactions in this experiment in which the following ions are detected:

a) CO_3^{2-}: _____

b) SO_4^{2-}: _____

c) Cl^-: _____

Simplest Formula of a Compound

Performance Goals

9–1 Prepare a compound and collect data from which you can determine the mass of each element in the compound.

9–2 From the mass of each element in a compound, determine its simplest formula.

CHEMICAL OVERVIEW

Chemical compounds are composed of atoms of different elements. The atoms are held together by chemical bonds. It has been shown experimentally that the ratio of moles of the elements in a compound is nearly always a ratio of small, whole numbers. The few exceptions are known as nonstoichiometric compounds. The formula containing the lowest possible ratio is known as its **simplest formula.** It is also called the **empirical formula.** At times it may be the same as the molecular formula; often, however, the molecular formula is an integral multiple of the simplest, empirical formula. For example, the simplest formula of the compound benzene (C_6H_6) is simply CH, indicating that the ratio of carbon atoms to hydrogen atoms is one to one.

To find the simplest formula of a compound, you will combine the elements in the compound under conditions that will allow you to determine the mass of each element. From these data the moles of atoms of each element may be calculated. By dividing these numbers by the smallest number of moles, you obtain quotients that are in a simple ratio of integers, or are readily converted to such a ratio. The ratio of moles of atoms of the elements in a compound is the same as the ratio of individual atoms that is expressed in the empirical formula.

> **Remember:** The essential information you require to find the simplest formula of a compound is the number of grams of each element in a sample of the compound.

In Option 1 you will react a measured mass of copper with excess sulfur. The excess sulfur is burned away as sulfur dioxide. In Option 2 the reaction is between a measured quantity of tin and excess nitric acid. The excess acid is boiled off. Option 3 involves the reaction of a measured mass of magnesium with excess oxygen from the air.

Your instructor may require you to perform the experiment twice to obtain duplicate results, or to complete more than one option. If so, plan your use of time. The procedure includes some periods in which you wait for a crucible to cool. The cooling periods in the first run of the experiment can be used for heating periods in the second run, and vice versa.

SAMPLE CALCULATIONS

A piece of aluminum is ignited in a suitable container, yielding an oxide. Calculate the simplest formula of the oxide from the following data:

Mass of container	17.84 g
Mass of container + aluminum	18.38 g
Mass of container + compound	18.86 g

1) Mass of each element from data:

$$\begin{array}{ccccc} \text{Mass of container} & & \text{mass of} & & \text{mass of} \\ \text{+ aluminum} & - & \text{container} & = & \text{aluminum} \\ \text{18.38 g} & - & \text{17.84 g} & = & \text{0.54 g aluminum} \end{array}$$

$$\begin{array}{ccccc} \text{Mass of container} & & \text{mass of container} & & \text{mass of} \\ \text{+ compound} & - & \text{+ aluminum} & = & \text{oxygen} \\ \text{18.86 g} & - & \text{18.38 g} & = & \text{0.48 g oxygen} \end{array}$$

2) Moles of each element:

$$0.54 \text{ g Al} \times \frac{1 \text{ mole Al atoms}}{27.0 \text{ g Al}} = 0.020 \text{ mole Al atoms}$$

$$0.48 \text{ g O} \times \frac{1 \text{ mole O atoms}}{16.0 \text{ g O}} = 0.030 \text{ mole O atoms}$$

3) Simplest formula ratio:

Obtain the ratio of atoms by dividing the number of moles of each atom by the smallest number of moles:

$$\text{Al:} \quad \frac{0.020}{0.020} = 1.0; \qquad \text{O:} \quad \frac{0.030}{0.020} = 1.5$$

The ratio is 1.0 mole aluminum atoms to 1.5 moles oxygen atoms. Change this ratio to a whole number ratio by multiplying each value by 2:

$$\text{moles of Al atoms} = 1.0 \times 2 = 2.0$$

$$\text{moles of O atoms} = 1.5 \times 2 = 3.0$$

The simplest formula is therefore Al_2O_3.

Many students find it convenient to organize their calculations by arranging both data and results in a table as follows:

Element	Grams	Moles	Mole Ratio	Formula Ratio
Al	0.54	0.020	1.0	2
O	0.48	0.030	1.5	3

SAFETY PRECAUTIONS AND DISPOSAL METHODS

The safety considerations in this experiment relate to the operation of a Bunsen burner and the handling of hot items. Blue burner flames are visible, but easily lost against a laboratory background. Be careful not to reach through one in reaching for some object behind it. If you have long hair, tie it back so it does not get into the flame. Be sure to use crucible tongs in handling hot crucibles, including the lid. Laboratory hardware gets hot, too. Harmful gases are released in Options 1 and 2. These reactions must be performed in a fume hood, as stated in their procedures. Be careful of hot chemical spattering from crucibles when they are heated. Be sure to wear goggles throughout this experiment.

Dispose of any solid residue as directed by your instructor.

PROCEDURE

OPTION 1:   A SULFIDE OF COPPER

Note: All mass measurements in Option 1 are to be recorded in grams to the nearest 0.01 g.

A)   The purpose of this step is to remove moisture from the crucible. Support a clean, dry porcelain crucible and its lid on a clay triangle, as shown in Figure 9–1. Heat it slowly at first, and then fairly strongly in the direct flame of a burner for about 4 to 5 minutes. Set the crucible and lid aside on a wire gauze to cool.

B)   When the crucible and lid are cool to the touch, weigh them on a centigram balance. Record this value as the mass of the container.

C)   Place a loosely rolled ball of copper wire or medium shavings, about 1.5 to 2 g, into the crucible. Weigh them, with the lid, on a centigram balance, and record the weight as the mass of the container plus metal.

D)   Sprinkle about 1 to 1.5 g of powdered sulfur over the copper. Place the lid on the crucible and begin heating it in a fume hood. Heat slowly at first, and then with a moderate flame until the sulfur no longer burns around the lid. Finally, heat the crucible strongly for about 5 minutes, making sure that no excess sulfur is present on the lid or on the sides of the crucible. It sometimes helps to hold the burner at its base and direct the flame under the lip of the lid all the way around.

E)   Set the container and its contents aside to cool. Do not open the lid until the crucible is cool, as air oxidation is apt to occur.

F)   When the crucible is cool, lift the lid and examine the contents. There should be no evidence of sulfur in the crucible or on the lid. If sulfur is present, heat the crucible again until the sulfur is completely burned away. Allow the crucible to cool.

G)   Weigh the container and its contents again. Record your measurement as the mass of the container plus compound.

H)   Set the container aside while you complete your calculations. Do not discard your compound until your calculations are finished and satisfactory; if they are not satisfactory, it is possible you may be able to salvage your work if the material is still on hand.

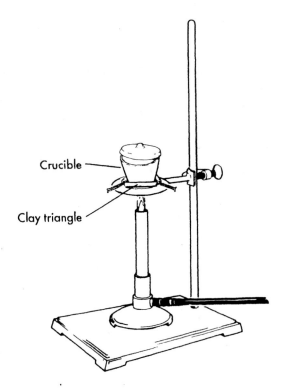

Crucible

Clay triangle

Figure 9—1   Heating of a porcelain crucible.

I) Just before discarding the compound, press it to the bottom of the crucible. Notice the difference between the physical properties of the compound and those of the elements from which it was formed. The compound should be discarded as directed by your instructor.

OPTION 2: AN OXIDE OF TIN

Note: All mass measurements in Option 2 are to be recorded in grams to the nearest 0.01 g.

A)   Heat a porcelain crucible and its lid as described in Option 1, Step A. Allow it to cool.

B)   Weigh as described in Option 1, Step B.

C)   Place a loosely rolled ball of tin foil, weighing 1 to 1.5 g, into the crucible. Weigh the crucible, the lid, and the metal on a centigram balance. Record the mass obtained.

D)   Under the fume hood, add concentrated nitric acid, HNO_3, drop by drop, to the crucible until all the tin has reacted and a damp white paste remains.

E)   Heat the paste cautiously with a mild flame, taking care not to cause spattering. After all of the liquid has evaporated, heat the crucible with a hot flame for 5 minutes.

F)   Cool the crucible and compound to room temperature and weigh it. Record the mass of the container and compound.

G)   Keep your compound in the crucible until all calculations are completed. This may save you time if it becomes necessary to add more nitric acid.

OPTION 3: MAGNESIUM OXIDE

Note: All mass measurements in Option 3 are to be recorded in grams to the nearest 0.01 g.

A)   Heat a porcelain crucible and its lid as described in Option 1, Step A. Allow it to cool.

B)   Weigh the crucible and lid on a *milligram* balance. Record this value on the report sheet as mass of the container.

C)   Place a loosely folded magnesium ribbon, weighing 0.5 to 0.7 g, into the crucible. Weigh the crucible, lid, and metal on a milligram balance and record the mass.

D)   Remove the lid and hold it near the crucible with a pair of tongs. Start heating the crucible, and as soon as the magnesium begins to burn, replace the lid. Continue the process, holding the escape of white smoke to a minimum (very finely divided magnesium oxide looks like smoke). When the contents of the crucible no longer burn, cock the lid wide enough to allow a sufficient amount of air to enter to complete the reaction, as shown in Figure 6–1, and heat it strongly for 5 minutes.

E)   To convert the possible side product, magnesium nitride, to the oxide, let the crucible cool, add 10 drops of deionized water to it and then gently heat to vaporize excess water. CAUTION: SPATTERING MAY OCCUR.

F)   Finish heating the crucible with a strong flame for 5 to 8 minutes.

G)   Weigh the cool crucible, lid, and product on a milligram balance.

Work Page

DATA

Option or Trial				
Mass of container (g)				
Mass of container + metal (g)				
Mass of container + compound (g)				

RESULTS FOR SAMPLE OF COMPOUND PREPARED

Mass of metal (g)				
Mass of nonmetal element (g)				
Moles of metal				
Moles of nonmetal element				
Ratio: $\dfrac{\text{moles metal}}{\text{moles nonmetal}}$ *	$\overline{}$ 1	$\overline{}$ 1	$\overline{}$ 1	$\overline{}$ 1
Simplest formula				

* Express this ratio as a decimal number over 1 (e.g., $\dfrac{3.044}{1}$), with the numerator to the number of significant figures justified by the data.

Show calculations on the reverse side of this page.

CALCULATIONS

Report Sheet

DATA

Option or Trial				
Mass of container (g)				
Mass of container + metal (g)				
Mass of container + compound (g)				

RESULTS FOR SAMPLE OF COMPOUND PREPARED

Mass of metal (g)				
Mass of nonmetal element (g)				
Moles of metal				
Moles of nonmetal element				
Ratio: $\dfrac{\text{moles metal}}{\text{moles nonmetal}}$ *	$\overline{}$ 1	$\overline{}$ 1	$\overline{}$ 1	$\overline{}$ 1
Simplest formula				

* Express this ratio as a decimal number over 1 (e.g., $\dfrac{3.044}{1}$), with the numerator to the number of significant figures justified by the data.

Show calculations on the reverse side of this page.

CALCULATIONS

Advance Study Assignment

1) Circle the one of the following formulas that is correctly written as an empirical formula:

$$NaSO_{1.5} \qquad (H_2NO)_2 \qquad Fe_3O_4$$

2) 6.25 grams of pure iron are allowed to react with oxygen to form an oxide. If the product weighs 14.31 grams, find the simplest formula of the compound.

3) In determining the simplest formula of lead sulfide, 2.46 grams of lead are placed in a crucible with 2.00 grams of sulfur. When the reaction is complete, the product has a mass of 3.22 grams. What mass of sulfur should be used in the simplest formula calculation? Find the simplest formula of lead sulfide.

Experiment **10**

Determination of a Chemical Formula

When atoms of one element combine with those of another, the combining ratio is typically an integer or a simple fraction; 1:2, 1:1, 2:1, and 2:3 are ratios one might encounter. The simplest formula of a compound expresses that atom ratio. Some substances with the ratios we listed include $CaCl_2$, KBr, Ag_2O, and Fe_2O_3. When more than two elements are present in a compound, the formula still indicates the atom ratio. Thus the substance with the formula Na_2SO_4 indicates that the sodium, sulfur, and oxygen atoms occur in that compound in the ratio 2:1:4. Many compounds have more complex formulas than those we have noted, but the same principles apply.

To find the formula of a compound we need to find the mass of each of the elements in a weighed sample of that compound. For example, if we resolved a sample of the compound NaOH weighing 40 grams into its elements, we would find that we obtained just about 23 grams of sodium, 16 grams of oxygen, and 1 gram of hydrogen. Since the atomic mass scale tells us that sodium atoms have a relative mass of 23, oxygen atoms a relative mass of 16, and hydrogen atoms a relative mass of just about 1, we would conclude that the sample of NaOH contained equal numbers of Na, O, and H atoms. Since that is the case, the atom ratio Na:O:H is 1:1:1, and so the simplest formula is NaOH. In terms of moles, we can say that that one mole of NaOH, 40 grams, contains one mole of Na, 23 grams, one mole of O, 16 grams, and one mole of H, 1 gram, where we define the mole to be that mass in grams equal numerically to the sum of the atomic masses in an element or a compound. From this kind of argument we can conclude that the atom ratio in a compound is equal to the mole ratio. We get the mole ratio from chemical analysis, and from that the formula of the compound.

In this experiment we will use these principles to find the formula of the compound with the general formula $Cu_xCl_y \cdot zH_2O$, where the x, y, and z are integers which, when known, establish the formula of the compound. (In expressing the formula of a compound like this one, where water molecules remain intact within the compound, we retain the formula of H_2O in the formula of the compound.)

The compound we will study, which is called copper chloride hydrate, turns out to be ideal for one's first venture into formula determination. It is stable, can be obtained in pure form, has a characteristic blue-green color which changes as the compound is changed chemically, and is relatively easy to decompose into the elements and water. In the experiment we will first drive out the water, which is called the water of hydration, from an accurately weighed sample of the compound. This occurs if we gently heat the sample to a little over 100°C. As the water is driven out, the color of the sample changes from blue-green to a tan-brown color similar to that of tobacco. The compound formed is anhydrous (no water) copper chloride. If we subtract its mass from that of the hydrate, we can determine the mass of the water that was driven off, and, using the molar mass of water, find the number of moles of H_2O that were in the sample.

In the next step we need to find either the mass of copper or the mass of chlorine in the anhydrous sample we have prepared. It turns out to be much easier to determine the mass of the copper, and find the mass of chlorine by difference. We do this by dissolving the anhydrous sample in water, which gives us a green solution containing copper and chloride ions. To that solution we add some aluminum metal wire. Aluminum is what we call an active metal; in contact with a solution containing copper ions, the aluminum metal will react chemically with those ions, converting them to copper metal. The aluminum is said to reduce the copper ions to the metal, and is itself oxidized. The copper metal appears on the wire as the reaction proceeds, and has the typical red-orange color. When the reaction is complete, we remove the excess Al, separate the copper from the solution, and weigh the dried metal. From its mass we can calculate the number of moles of copper in the sample. We find the mass of chlorine by subtracting the mass of copper from that of the anhydrous copper chloride, and from that value determine the number of moles of chlorine. The mole ratio for Cu:Cl:H_2O gives us the formula of the compound.

Experimental Procedure: WEAR YOUR SAFETY GLASSES WHILE YOU PERFORM THE EXPERIMENT!

1.   Weigh a clean, dry crucible without the cover and **record its mass in grams.**to 3 decimal places.

2.   Add about 1 gram of the hydrated copper chloride to the crucible. **Record the original color** of the hydrated crystals. Break up any big pieces. Weigh the crucible and the hydrated copper chloride to 3 decimal places. **Record the mass.** <u>NOTE</u>: The difference between this mass and the mass of the empty crucible in step 1 equals the mass of the hydrated sample.

3.   Place the crucible with the hydrate on a clay triangle supported by an iron ring. **Gently heat** the crucible with the hydrated copper chloride with a Bunsen burner. After **ALL** the hydrate has turned light brown (or tan), gently heat for another 2 minutes. **Record the color** of the sample. Cover the crucible and let it cool for 15 minutes. <u>NOTE</u>: If the hydrate begins to turn black, it has been heated too much.

4.   Take the cover off the crucible. Weigh the crucible and its contents to 3 decimal places. **Record the mass.** <u>NOTE</u>: The difference between this mass and the mass of the empty crucible in step 1 is the mass of the dehydrated sample. The difference between the mass of the hydrated sample calculated in step **2** and the weight of the dehydrated sample calculated in this step (**4**) is the mass of the water expelled from the hydrated sample.

5.   Transfer the brown crystals (dehydrated sample) from the crucible to an empty 50 mL beaker. Use a spatula to help. Rinse out the crucible with two to three 5 mL portions of distilled water to dissolve and transfer any remaining sample into the 50 mL beaker. The water will dissolve the crystals. **Record the color** of the solution; it will now be green. **No more crystals should remain in the crucible.**

6.   Measure an 8 to 9 inch length of aluminum wire. Form the wire into a loose coil and immerse it in the solution in the beaker. **Record the colors** of the copper metal that collects on the wire. Allow the reaction to **continue until the solution is colorless.** If necessary, you may use a second piece of aluminum wire.

7.   Use a glass rod to dislodge the copper from the aluminum wire so that falls to the bottom of the beaker. If necessary, place a few drops of 6M HCl on the wire to remove the copper. Do your best to collect all the copper from the aluminum wire. Then remove any remaining unreacted aluminum wire.

8.   Weigh a <u>dry</u> piece of filter paper and **record its mass** to 3 decimal places. Set up a Buchner funnel as directed and put the filter paper in it. Gently wet the filter paper with a few milliliters of distilled water and briefly apply suction (vacuum) with the aspirator to seal the paper to the bottom of the funnel.

9.   Slowly pour the liquid mixture with the solid copper into the filter so that all the copper ends up **near the center of the filter paper**. Turn on the aspirator to suck any liquid from the funnel.

10. With the aspirator suction still on, gently wash any remaining copper onto the filter paper in the funnel with small amounts of distilled water using a dropper or a wash bottle.

11. Turn off the suction on the Buchner funnel. Add 10 mL of ethanol to the filter paper. Wait about one minute and turn the suction back on for a few minutes. The ethanol will dissolve and wash off the excess water from the solid copper. It will also evaporate easily so the solid sample will dry more quickly.

12. Carefully lift the filter paper from the funnel to avoid losing any copper. Put the paper with the copper under a heat lamp for 5 minutes until it is <u>completely</u> dry. Weigh the filter paper and copper to 3 decimal places. **Record this value.** <u>NOTE</u>: The mass of the copper is the difference between this weight and the weight of the dry filter paper in step **8**. The mass of the chloride is the difference between the mass of the dehydrated sample calculated in step **4** and the mass of the copper calculated in step **12**.

Dispose of all liquid & solid waste products from the experiment as directed by your lab instructor.

Data and calculations: Experiment 10 rv   **Determination of a Chemical Formula**

Atomic masses (molar masses) in g/mol: **Cu** = 63.55;   **Cl** = 35.45;   **H** = 1.008;   **O** = 16.00

  [**Note:** Number of moles (of an element *or* a compound) = mass divided by atomic mass (molar mass)]

....

A: Mass of empty crucible [step **1**]: _____ g

B: Mass of crucible and hydrated sample [step **2**]: _____ g

C: Mass of hydrated sample [**B – A**]: _____ g [Cu, Cl, & H$_2$O]

D: Mass of crucible and dehydrated sample [step **4**]: _____ g

E: Mass of dehydrated sample [**D – A**]: _____ g [Cu & Cl]

F: Mass of **water** [**E – C**]: _____ g;   **G:**   moles of **water**: _____ mol

H: Mass of dry filter paper [step **8**]: _____ g

I: Mass of filter paper and solid copper [step **12**]: _____ g

J: Mass of **copper** [**I – H**]: _____ g;   **K:**   moles of **copper**: _____ mol

L: Mass of **chlorine** [**E - J**]: _____ g;   **M:**   moles of **chlorine**: _____ mol

N: Calculate the mole ratio of Cl/Cu in the sample [= **M/K**]: _____ mol

O: Calculate the mole ratio of water to Cu in the hydrated sample [= **F/K**]: _____ mol

P: Write formula of dehydrated compound (round to the nearest integer): _____

Q: Write formula of hydrated compound (round to the nearest integer): _____

Advance Study Assignment: Determination of a Chemical Formula

1. To find the mass of a mole of an element, one looks up the atomic mass of the element in a table of atomic masses (see Appendix III or the Periodic Table). The molar mass of an element is simply the mass in grams of that element that is numerically equal to its atomic mass. For a compound substance, the molar mass is equal to the mass in grams that is numerically equal to the sum of the atomic masses in the formula of the substance. Find the molar mass of

    Cu _____ g   Cl _____ g   H _____ g   O _____ g H_2O _____ g

2. If one can find the ratio of the number of moles of the elements in a compound to one another, one can find the formula of the compound. In a certain compound of copper and oxygen, Cu_xO_y, we find that a sample weighing 0.5424 g contains 0.4831 g Cu.

    a. How many moles of Cu are there in the sample?

    $$\left(\text{No. moles} = \frac{\text{mass Cu}}{\text{molar mass Cu}} \right)$$

    _____ moles

    b. How many grams of O are there in the sample? (The mass of the sample equals the mass of Cu plus the mass of O.)

    _____ g

    c. How many moles of O are there in the sample?

    _____ moles

    d. What is the mole ratio (no. moles Cu/no. moles O) in the sample?

    _____ : 1

    e. What is the formula of the oxide? (The atom ratio equals the mole ratio, and is expressed using the smallest integers possible.)

    _____

    f. What is the molar mass of the copper oxide?

    _____ g

Molar Mass of a Volatile Liquid

Performance Goals

11-1   Determine experimentally the mass of a vapor occupying a known volume at a given temperature and pressure.

11-2   Calculate the molar mass of a volatile liquid from the mass of a given volume of vapor at a measured temperature and pressure.

CHEMICAL OVERVIEW

An "ideal gas" is one that behaves as if the molecules (a) are widely separated from each other, (b) have negligible volumes of their own compared to the space they occupy, and (c) are not subject to intermolecular attractive or repulsive forces. Under ordinary conditions in the laboratory, most gases approach the behavior of ideal gases.

In describing the behavior of gases, four variables must be considered: (a) volume, V, (b) pressure, P, (c) absolute temperature, T, and (d) amount, measured in number of moles, n. Considering the separate relationships between volume and each of the other three variables, we derive these laws:

Volume is inversely proportional to pressure at constant temperature and amount (Boyle's Law):

$$V \propto \frac{1}{P} \tag{11.1}$$

This means, for example, that the higher the pressure on a given amount of gas (at constant T), the smaller a volume the gas will occupy.

Volume is directly proportional to absolute temperature (K) at constant pressure and amount (Charles' Law):

$$V \propto T \tag{11.2}$$

For example, if you heat a given amount of gas at constant pressure, the volume will increase.

Volume is directly proportional to the amount of gas at constant pressure and temperature:

$$V \propto n \tag{11.3}$$

In other words, the more gas there is (at constant T and P), the larger a volume it will occupy. Combining these relationships yields the ideal gas equation:

$$PV = nRT \tag{11.4}$$

where R is a proportionality constant.

The units of R depend upon the units used in measuring the four variables. In working with gases in chemistry, you will measure volume in liters and temperature in degrees Celsius, which will be converted to Kelvins. If pressure is measured in atmospheres,

$$R = 0.0821 \, \frac{\text{(liter)(atmosphere)}}{\text{(K)(mole)}} \qquad (11.5)$$

If, on the other hand, pressure is measured in mm Hg (torr),

$$R = 62.4 \, \frac{\text{(liter)(torr)}}{\text{(K)(mole)}} \qquad (11.6)$$

The numerical value of R is the same for all gases, pure or mixtures.

A useful variation of the ideal gas equation may be derived as follows: If the mass of any chemical species, g, is divided by the molar mass, MM, the quotient is the number of moles.

$$\frac{g}{MM} = \frac{\text{grams}}{\text{grams/mole}} = \text{moles}$$

Therefore, for any pure gas, $\dfrac{g}{MM}$ may be substituted for its equivalent, n, in Equation 18.4:

$$PV = \frac{g}{MM} \, RT \qquad (11.7)$$

This equation can be used to determine the molar mass of a gas or compound that is readily converted to a vapor.

In this experiment, you will place a volatile liquid into a flask of measured volume and immerse the flask in boiling water. The liquid will vaporize and drive the air out of the flask, filling the entire volume with vapor. The mass of the vapor will be measured by condensing it and weighing it. With pressure, volume, temperature, and mass all known, molar mass may be determined by direct substitution into Equation 11.7.

SAMPLE CALCULATION

Find the molar mass of a gas if a 0.895-g sample occupies 235 mL at 95°C and 1.02 atmospheres pressure.

Substitution into Equation 11.7 requires that volumes be measured in liters and temperature in Kelvins. These conversions are:

$$V = 235 \text{ mL} \times \frac{1 \text{ liter}}{1000 \text{ mL}} = 0.235 \text{ liter}$$

$$K = {}°C + 273 = 95 + 273 = 386 \text{ K}$$

Solving Equation 11.7 for molar mass and substituting the experimental values yields

$$MM = \frac{gRT}{PV} = \frac{0.895 \text{ g}}{1.02 \text{ atm}} \times \frac{0.0821 \text{ (liter)(atm)}}{\text{(K)(mole)}} \times \frac{368 \text{ K}}{0.235 \text{ liter}} = 113 \text{ g/mole}$$

In calculations with the ideal gas equation, be sure to include units. This will enable you to check whether you are setting up the problem correctly. If not, the unit of the quantity calculated will not be correct and you will know that you must recheck your setup for errors.

SAFETY PRECAUTIONS AND DISPOSAL METHODS

Be careful when handling volatile liquids. Many of these compounds can be harmful when their vapors are inhaled. Also, extreme care should be used when dealing with boiling water. If you should have to move the beaker with boiling water in it, be sure to hold the beaker securely.

Dispose of excess liquids in a stoppered bottle in the fume hood. *Do not pour liquids down the drain.*

PROCEDURE

Note: Record temperature in degrees Celsius to the nearest degree; pressure in torr to the nearest torr; mass in grams to the nearest 0.001 g; and volume in milliliters to the nearest milliliter.

A)   Weigh a clean, dry 125-mL Erlenmeyer flask, along with a 5-cm × 5-cm square of aluminum foil, on a milligram balance; record the mass on the report sheet.

B)   Obtain 4 to 5 mL of an unknown liquid from the instructor and place it in the flask. Record the number of the unknown. Crimp the aluminum foil fairly tightly around the neck of the flask and punch a *tiny* hole with a pin in the center of the foil.

C)   Fill a 600-mL beaker about 1/3 full of water. Clamp the Erlenmeyer flask to a ring stand and immerse it in the beaker, as shown in Figure 11–1. Add more water until the flask is totally immersed, but not so deep that the water reaches the lower edge of the foil.

D)   Remove the flask from the beaker and heat the water to boiling. Return the flask to its former position in the beaker and continue heating.

E)   Measure and record the temperature of the boiling water and the barometric pressure.

F)   As soon as *all* liquid in the flask has vaporized (no condensed beads of liquid on the walls or neck of the flask), remove the flask from the water and allow it to cool to room temperature. You may find it necessary to remove the flask from the beaker a few times to inspect it for remaining liquid, returning it promptly if liquid is present. Do not heat the flask too long, as this will lead to erroneous results.

G)   As the flask cools, carefully wipe the outside, making sure that no water droplets have collected under the edge of the aluminum foil. When the flask is at room temperature, weigh the flask, foil, and condensed liquid on a milligram balance and record the mass on your report sheet.

H)   To establish the volume of the gas, fill the flask completely with water and then measure its volume using a graduated cylinder. Record your reading to the nearest milliliter.

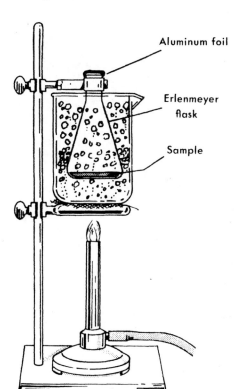

Figure 11—1. Apparatus for determining the molar mass of a volatile liquid.

CALCULATIONS

From the data, determine the volume of the gas in liters and the vapor temperature in Kelvins. (Assume the temperature is the same as that of the boiling water in which the flask was immersed.) Then find the molar mass, as shown in the sample calculation.

Work Page

Unknown No. _____

DATA

Run	1	2	3
Mass of flask and foil (g)			
Mass of flask and foil and condensed vapor (g)			
Temperature of boiling water (°C)			
Barometric pressure (torr)			
Volume of flask (mL)			

RESULTS

Mass of unknown (condensed vapor) (g)			
Volume of flask (vapor) (L)			
Temperature of vapor (K)			
Molar mass of unknown (g/mole)			

Show complete calculations for one column from the above tables:

Report Sheet

Unknown No. _____

DATA

Run	1	2	3
Mass of flask and foil (g)			
Mass of flask and foil and condensed vapor (g)			
Temperature of boiling water (°C)			
Barometric pressure (torr)			
Volume of flask (mL)			

RESULTS

Mass of unknown (condensed vapor) (g)			
Volume of flask (vapor) (L)			
Temperature of vapor (K)			
Molar mass of unknown (g/mole)			

Show complete calculations for one column from the above tables:

Advance Study Assignment

1) How would each of the following errors affect the outcome of this experiment? Would it make the molar mass high or low? Give your reasoning in three sentences or less in each case.

   a) The hole in the aluminum foil was quite large.

   b) Water vapors condensed under the aluminum foil before the final weighing.

2) A volatile liquid was allowed to evaporate in a 43.298 g flask that has a total volume of 252 mL. The temperature of the water bath was 100°C at the atmospheric pressure of 776 torr. The mass of the flask and condensed vapor was 44.173 g. Calculate the molar mass of the liquid.

Titration of Acids and Bases—I

Performance Goals

12–1   Given the volume of a solution of known molarity, and the volume to which it is diluted with water, calculate the molarity of the diluted solution.

12–2   Given the approximate molarity and volume of an acid or base solution to be used in a titration, calculate the number of grams of a known solid base or acid required for the reaction.

12–3   Given the volume of a base or acid solution that reacts with a weighed quantity of a primary standard acid or base, calculate the molarity of the base or acid solution.

12–4   Perform acid–base titrations reproducibly.

CHEMICAL OVERVIEW

In this experiment you will prepare a standard solution of sodium hydroxide to be used in Experiment 24. Solid sodium hydroxide has the property of absorbing moisture from the air. It is therefore not possible to weigh sodium hydroxide accurately, which makes it unsuitable as a primary standard. Consequently, you will use the second of the two methods for preparing a standard solution listed on page 270. Your primary standard will be oxalic acid dihydrate, $H_2C_2O_4 \cdot 2\,H_2O$. The reaction between the acid and base is

$$2\,NaOH(aq) + H_2C_2O_4(aq) \rightarrow 2\,H_2O(\ell) + Na_2C_2O_4(aq) \tag{12.1}$$

Sodium hydroxide will be made available in the laboratory in the form of a solution that is approximately one molar (1 M) in concentration. Note that this is an *approximate* concentration, expressed in *one* significant figure. No calculation based on that concentration can be considered reliable. You will be instructed to dilute a specified quantity of that solution to a larger volume with water, and then to calculate the *approximate* concentration of the diluted solution (see Performance Goal 12–1). This is one of two preliminary calculations in this experiment, and it appears as Question 1 in the Advance Study Assignment. If you turn in your Advance Study Assignment at the beginning of the laboratory period, be sure to keep a copy of your calculation for use while performing the experiment. The diluted NaOH solution will be used in the titration.

Next it will be necessary for you to calculate the quantity of solid oxalic acid dihydrate, $H_2C_2O_4 \cdot 2\,H_2O$, that will react with approximately 15 mL of the diluted NaOH solution. This is a solution stoichiometry problem in which the first step is to find the number of moles of NaOH in 15 mL of solution at the approximate concentration just determined. The volume of a solution times its molarity yields the number of moles:

$$\text{Volume (liter)} \times \text{molarity}\left(\frac{\text{moles}}{\text{liter}}\right) = \text{moles} \tag{12.2}$$

The balance of the problem is set up and solved in the usual stoichiometry pattern. This is the second of the two preliminary calculations, and it corresponds to Performance Goal 12-2. This calculation appears as Question 2 in the Advance Study Assignment. Again, be sure to keep a copy for use while performing the experiment.

After carefully weighing out three samples of solid oxalic acid dihydrate, you will dissolve it and perform the titration described by Equation 12.1. From the mass of oxalic acid you will be able to determine the number of moles of acid present. From the equation you will determine the number of moles of NaOH required in the neutralization. You will then know both the volume of the NaOH solution and the number of moles of NaOH it contains. These are the "two essential items you require for (the) calculation of molarity" (see Introduction, p. 269): dividing moles by liters yields molarity. (See Performance Goal 12–3.)

The last of the performance goals for this experiment calls for you to perform titrations reproducibly. To meet this requirement you must come up with sodium hydroxide concentrations that are "the same" in separate titrations. This calls for establishing a standard of "sameness." You will be instructed to conduct three titrations as a minimum. If two of these yield molarities that are within 0.007 M of each other, they will be accepted as satisfying the reproducibility requirement. If you do not reach this result, additional titrations will be required.

So far nothing has been mentioned about the *accuracy* of your work. Indeed, within Experiment 12 there is no way to judge accuracy, as each student will have his/her own sodium hydroxide solution, which will have a concentration slightly different from that of his/her neighbor. In Experiment 24, however, you will use your standard solution to determine the concentration of an acid that is unknown to you, *but known to your instructor.* At this point an accurate result will be required. It should be apparent that your result in Experiment 24 cannot be accurate unless the concentration of the solution prepared in Experiment 12 has been determined accurately. As a consequence, if your accuracy in Experiment 24 does not meet the standard established, *it may be necessary for you to repeat Experiment 12 in order to correct previously undetected errors made there.* With this in mind, you are strongly urged to retain a complete record of *all* data, *all* volumes in the titrations, even if you think them to be incorrect. It is surprising how often "incorrect" data turn out to be just what is needed by the time a long experiment is completed.

SAMPLE CALCULATIONS

The following examples illustrate the calculations involved in Performance Goals 12–1 and 12–3:

Example 1

25.0 mL of a 12.0 M solution is diluted to 500 mL. Calculate the molarity of the dilute solution.

The number of moles of solute is the same in both the initial solution and the diluted solution; only water is added. This number of moles is

$$0.0250 \text{ L} \times \frac{12.0 \text{ moles}}{\text{L}} = 0.300 \text{ mole}$$

In the diluted solution the 0.300 mole of solute is dissolved in 500 mL, or 0.500 L. The concentration is therefore

$$\frac{0.300 \text{ mole}}{0.500 \text{ L}} = 0.600 \text{ mole/L}$$

Example 2

Calculate the molarity of an NaOH solution if a sample of oxalic acid weighing 1.235 g requires 42.5 mL of the base for neutralization.

First, determine the number of moles of oxalic acid present. The formula of solid oxalic acid is $H_2C_2O_4 \cdot 2 H_2O$. Notice that, although the water of hydration is not shown in Equation 12.1, the acid is weighed as a solid, which includes the water. Accordingly, calculations must be based on the proper molar mass. Thus,

$$1.235 \text{ g H}_2\text{C}_2\text{O}_4 \cdot 2\text{ H}_2\text{O} \times \frac{1 \text{ mole H}_2\text{C}_2\text{O}_4}{126 \text{ g H}_2\text{C}_2\text{O}_4 \cdot 2\text{ H}_2\text{O}} = 0.00980 \text{ mole H}_2\text{C}_2\text{O}_4$$

Second, determine the number of moles of NaOH required to react with 0.00980 mole of $\text{H}_2\text{C}_2\text{O}_4$, according to the equation.

$$0.00980 \text{ mole H}_2\text{C}_2\text{O}_4 \times \frac{2 \text{ moles NaOH}}{1 \text{ mole H}_2\text{C}_2\text{O}_4} = 0.0196 \text{ mole NaOH}$$

Third, if 0.0196 mole of NaOH is present in 42.5 mL of solution, find the concentration in moles per *liter.*

$$\frac{0.0196 \text{ mole NaOH}}{0.0425 \text{ L}} = 0.461 \text{ M NaOH}$$

As a single dimensional analysis setup, this calculation would appear as:

$$1.235 \text{ g H}_2\text{C}_2\text{O}_4 \cdot 2\text{ H}_2\text{O} \times \frac{1 \text{ mole H}_2\text{C}_2\text{O}_4}{126 \text{ g H}_2\text{C}_2\text{O}_4 \cdot 2\text{ H}_2\text{O}} \times \frac{2 \text{ moles NaOH}}{1 \text{ mole H}_2\text{C}_2\text{O}_4} \times \frac{1}{0.0425 \text{ L}} = 0.461 \text{ M NaOH}$$

SAFETY PRECAUTIONS AND DISPOSAL METHODS

If some of the sodium hydroxide solution, either concentrated or dilute, comes into contact with your skin, it will have a slippery feeling, somewhat like soap. This is produced because the solution is slowly dissolving a layer of your skin. For obvious reasons, the process should not be allowed to continue. If you encounter that feeling at any time during the experiment, take time out to wash your hands thoroughly until the slippery feeling is gone.

Both the acid and base used in this experiment are corrosive and harmful over prolonged exposure. Avoid all unnecessary contact, and keep them off your clothing too. Both solutions are harmful to the eyes; be sure to wear goggles when working with all chemicals, either solid or in solution, during this experiment. The goggle requirement extends to cleaning-up operations, at which time bristles of buret brushes have been known to flick drops of chemicals into unprotected eyes.

After you have finished the titrations, SAVE your NaOH solution for Experiment 24. The content of the Erlenmeyer flasks can be poured down the drain.

PROCEDURE

Note: Record all mass measurements in grams to the nearest 0.001 g. Record all volume measurements from the buret in milliliters to the nearest 0.1 mL.

1. PREPARATION OF NaOH SOLUTION

A) Using a graduated cylinder, transfer about 100 mL of 1 M NaOH to a large beaker (600 mL or larger). With continuous stirring, dilute with deionized water until the total volume is about 500 mL.

Note: Thorough mixing is essential at this point. If you determine the "concentration" of an unmixed solution, you determine the concentration of only that part of the solution that you use. If you then use another part of the solution, with a different concentration, you will have no accuracy in your second application.

B) Transfer your solution to a stoppered or capped storage bottle. (Always keep your standard solution covered, as any evaporation loss or CO_2 absorption will change its concentration.) Label the bottle with your name, so it does not become lost among the bottles of your laboratory neighbors.

C) Calculate the approximate molarity of your solution. (This is Question 1 in the Advance Study Assignment.)

2. PREPARATION OF OXALIC ACID SOLUTIONS

A)   From the approximate molarity of the diluted NaOH solution, calculate the mass of oxalic acid dihydrate, $H_2C_2O_4 \cdot 2\,H_2O$, needed to neutralize 15 mL of the base. Don't forget the water of hydration in the solid acid, as it will be present in what you weigh out. Have your instructor approve your calculation before proceeding. (This is Question 2 in the Advance Study Assignment.)

B)   Make identifying marks on three 250-mL Erlenmeyer flasks.

Note: The next step is extremely critical. Your purpose is to transfer into each of the above Erlenmeyer flasks an amount of oxalic acid dihydrate that is approximately equal to what was calculated in Step 2A, but whose actual mass is known to the closest milligram. Be sure you understand that purpose and the procedure below by which it will be accomplished. The care with which this step is performed will determine both the accuracy and precision with which your sodium hydroxide solution is standardized, and the accuracy of your result in Experiment 24. Be particularly careful that no oxalic acid is spilled. If that happens, begin again.

C)   Transfer four to five times the amount of oxalic acid dihydrate calculated in Step 2A into a small (preferably 50 mL or less), clean, dry beaker. Weigh the beaker and its contents on a milligram balance to the closest 0.001 g. Record the mass in the data table as "Mass of beaker + acid." Transfer from the beaker to one of the marked Erlenmeyer flasks a quantity of acid that is within 10 percent of the amount calculated in Step 2A by gently tapping the beaker. *Do not* use a spatula for the transfer or crystals will be lost on it. (Do not attempt to transfer exactly the calculated amount.) Weigh the beaker and its contents again, recording the measurement as "Mass of beaker − acid" for the first flask, and also as "Mass of beaker + acid" for the second flask. Again transfer the required amount of oxalic acid dihydrate, this time to the second Erlenmeyer flask. Weigh the beaker and its contents, recording the mass as "Mass of beaker − acid" for the second flask, and as "Mass of beaker + acid" for the third flask. Repeat the procedure once more to get the "Mass of beaker − acid" for the third flask.

D)   Add about 50 mL of deionized water to each flask and swirl until the acid is dissolved. Be careful not to spill any water, which will take with it some of the weighed acid. (How important is the volume of water in which the acid is dissolved? How will the amount of water influence the number of milliliters of NaOH required to react with the quantity of acid in each flask?)

3. TITRATION OF OXALIC ACID WITH NaOH

A)   Thoroughly clean your buret. Rinse the buret with about 10 mL of the NaOH solution. Drain and repeat with a second portion, discarding it as well. Fill the buret with the NaOH solution you prepared. Drain the solution into the calibrated part of the buret, letting the liquid flow through the tip. Make sure the tip of the buret is filled, and that there are no bubbles. Then record the initial buret reading to the nearest 0.1 mL.

B)   Add 3 to 5 drops of phenolphthalein to each oxalic acid solution.

C)   Hold one of the Erlenmeyer flasks so that the tip of the buret is inside the neck portion of the flask, as in Figure 12–1. Start the addition of NaOH. At the beginning of the titration you may add the base in larger portions, slowing down as the time required for the pink color to disappear gets longer. It is essential that you swirl the contents of the flask vigorously throughout the titration to assure complete mixing of the solutions. The end of the titration is reached when the pink color persists for 30 seconds. Record the buret reading at this point.

D)   Repeat Step C with the other two samples. You may begin the titration from the volume reading on the buret at which the first titration ended. Be sure to record this value and make sure sufficient solution is available in the buret to complete the titration.

E)   Calculate the results of your first three runs immediately. If you do not have two NaOH molarities within 0.007 of each other, repeat Parts 2 and 3 until reproducible results are obtained. *Keep all titration data!*

If you satisfy the reproducibility requirement, proceed to Experiment 24. If that experiment is to be done at another time, store your NaOH solution (see Step 1B). Clean all glassware thoroughly before putting it away or returning it to the stockroom.

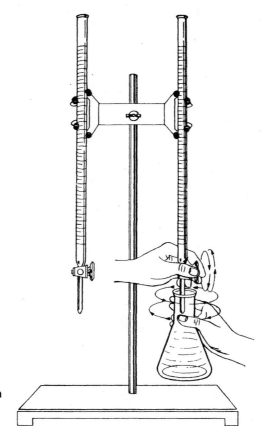

Figure 12—1. Titration from a buret into a flask.

Work Page

TABLE OF DATA AND RESULTS (Beneath the table show the full calculation setup for at least one valid titration run)

Sample	1	2	3	4	5	6	7	8
Mass of beaker + acid (g)								
Mass of beaker − acid (g)								
Mass of oxalic acid (g)								
Initial buret reading (mL)								
Final buret reading (mL)								
Volume of NaOH (mL)								
Molarity of NaOH								

Calculation setup for at least one valid titration run:

Report Sheet

TABLE OF DATA AND RESULTS (Beneath the table show the full calculation setup for at least one valid titration run)

Sample	1	2	3	4	5	6	7	8
Mass of beaker + acid (g)								
Mass of beaker − acid (g)								
Mass of oxalic acid (g)								
Initial buret reading (mL)								
Final buret reading (mL)								
Volume of NaOH (mL)								
Molarity of NaOH								

Calculation setup for at least one valid titration run:

Advance Study Assignment

1) Read Procedure 1 for the preparation of your NaOH solution. Calculate the approximate molarity of the solution (Step 1C). Do not round off your result to the proper number of significant figures at this point.

2) Using your result from the problem above, calculate the mass of oxalic acid dihydrate, $H_2C_2O_4 \cdot 2\,H_2O$, required to react with 15 mL of your NaOH solution (Step 2A in the procedure). Round off your final answer, taking into account the information in Problem 1 as well as this one. It is this result that must be approved by your instructor before you go beyond Step 2A in the procedure.

3) If 0.628 g of $H_2C_2O_4 \cdot 2\,H_2O$ requires 24.7 mL of NaOH(aq) in a titration, calculate the molarity of the solution.

4) Why must you save your NaOH solution at the end of Experiment 23?

5) If your fingers feel slippery at any time during this experiment, what does that indicate and what should you do about it?

13

Titration of an Acid with a Base

OBJECTIVE

To become familiar with a precise analytical technique.
To determine the amount of acid in a solution by titration.

APPARATUS AND CHEMICALS

50-mL buret (2)
buret clamp
ring stand
250-mL flask (3)
2 small funnels

250-mL beakers (2)
phenolphthalein solution
standard sodium hydroxide solution
unknown solution of hydrochloric acid

SAFETY CONSIDERATIONS

Use care in handling all glassware to prevent breakage. The burets can be broken at the clamp if excess pressure is applied.

The acid and base used in this experiment are dilute enough that they do not pose a serious hazard to skin and clothes if washed off quickly. However, either can cause serious and immediate damage to the sensitive tissues of the eyes. Safety glasses must be worn at all times, and if acid or base does get into the eyes, the eyes must be flushed immediately for 15 minutes with cold water and the instructor notified at once.

FACTS TO KNOW

The word *titration* is derived from a French word, *titre*, which means "to bestow a title upon or to standardize." The purpose of a chemical titration is to standardize a solution, that is, to determine the concentration of a substance in a solution. The *concentration* of a substance in a solution is the *amount* of the substance dissolved in a certain *volume* of solution. Often, concentrations of solutions are given in terms of molarity, M, which is defined as the number of gram molecular weights (or moles) in a liter of solution. For example, the molecular weight of HCl is 36.5. If 73 g (2 × 36.5) are dissolved in sufficient water to make a liter of solution, the concentration of the HCl in the solution is 2 molar (2 M), since 2 molecular weights in grams (or moles) are dissolved in the liter of solution.

In this experiment, the concentration of an acid in a solution will be determined by measuring the amount of acid solution required to react completely with a known amount of base. The acid will be hydrochloric acid, an important component of the digestive juices of the stomach, and the base will be sodium hydroxide, commonly known as lye. The equation for the reaction between hydrochloric acid and sodium hydroxide can be written

$$HCl + NaOH \rightarrow H_2O + NaCl$$

In order to determine the amount of hydrochloric acid in a solution, we must first measure a precise volume of this unknown acid. The second step requires that we add just enough sodium hydroxide solution of known concentration (standard solution) to neutralize the acid. This standard solution of sodium hydroxide has been carefully prepared to contain a rather exact amount of sodium hydroxide per liter of solution. Since we know the amount of sodium hydroxide per liter and the volume required to neutralize the measured volume of unknown hydrochloric acid concentration, we can calculate the amount of sodium hydroxide needed by multiplying the concentration of the standard base by the measured volume required for neutralization of the acid. For example,

$$amount/volume \times volume = amount,$$

or

$$concentration \times volume = amount.$$

When sufficient base solution has been added to neutralize completely the amount of acid present, a visual indicator changes color to signal that all of the base has reacted. In this experiment, the indicator, phenolphthalein, is pink in basic solution and colorless in acidic solution. Hence, when the solution is a very faint pink, sufficient sodium hydroxide has been added to the solution of hydrochloric acid to just neutralize the HCl and have a very slight amount of NaOH left over.

Volumes of solutions can be measured easily to an accuracy of ± 0.02 mL by using burets like those shown in Figure 15-1. To read a buret, have your eye level with the *bottom* of the curved surface of the liquid (the meniscus). To check the level of your eye, use the rings marked on the buret. If the ring nearest the meniscus appears to be a straight line, then your eye is at the proper height to read the buret. Now, place a contrast card behind the buret, as shown in Figure 15-2. The black portion is held just below the bottom of the meniscus, so that the meniscus appears to be black against a white background. Read the volume to two decimal places. The second decimal place (the hundredths place) is estimated by mentally dividing the space between two lines into ten equal parts, and counting the number of these parts required to go from the line just above the meniscus to the bottom of the meniscus.

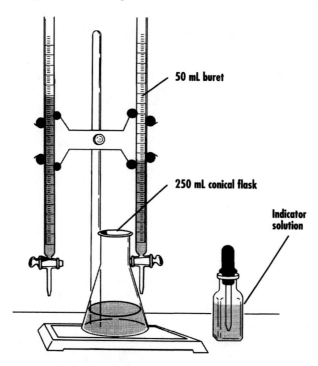

Figure 15-1. Equipment for titration.

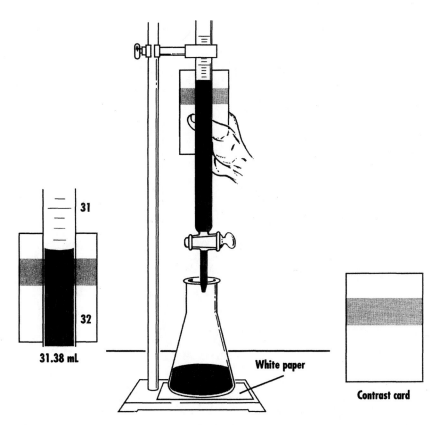

Figure 15-2. Proper use of a contrast card to read volumes.

31.38 mL

White paper

Contrast card

31

32

To gain a clear understanding of the process of a titration and the reasons for the calculations you will make, consider the following simplified titration.

Suppose you know that 1 atom (or ion) of acid A reacts with 1 atom (or ion) of base B to form a molecule of AB. That is:

$$A + B \rightarrow AB$$

Now suppose that we have a solution of A containing 3 A's per mL and a solution of B containing 2 B's per mL as shown in Figure 15-3.

Begin the titration by running in 3 mL of A and then add an indicator (Fig. 15-4). At this point we have 9 A's to be neutralized by the base; that is:

$$\text{amount of A} = (\text{concentration of A}) \times (\text{volume of A})$$

$$= \frac{3 \text{ A's}}{\text{mL}} \times 3 \text{ mL}$$

$$= 9 \text{ A's}$$

Now add solution containing B until you have just as many B's in solution as you have A's, that is, until you have only AB's in solution, with no excess of either A or B. If a very slight excess of B is added, the indicator changes color.

How many mL of B do we have to add? We have to add enough mL of B to give 9 B's, to match the 9 A's previously added. This means that we have to add 4.5 mL of B (Fig. 15-5). At the endpoint,

$$\text{amount of A} = \text{amount of B}$$

$$9 \text{ A's} = \frac{2B}{\text{mL}} \times 4.5 \text{ mL}$$

$$9 \text{ A's} = 9 \text{ B's}$$

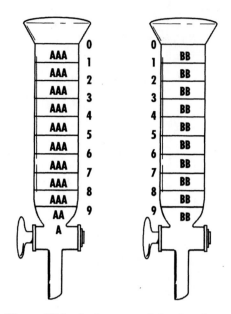

Figure 15-3. At the start of the titration.

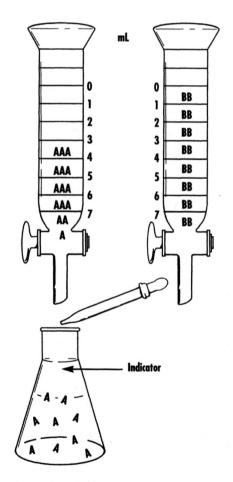

Figure 15-4. After A's have added to flask.

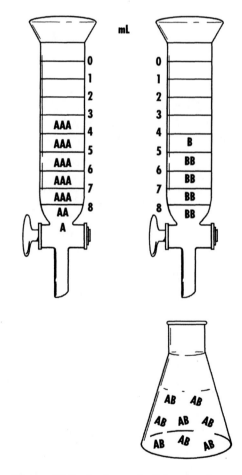

Figure 15-5. At the end of the titration.

132

In this example, both concentrations were known, but normally in a titration only one concentration is known, along with the volume of A and the volume of B required to reach an endpoint. The volumes can always be determined in the laboratory. The basis for calculating the concentration of a substance of unknown concentration (the hydrochloric acid, in this experiment) is exactly the same as in the example.

At the endpoint,

$$\text{amount of acid} = \text{amount of base}$$

$$\text{concentration of acid} \times \text{volume of acid} = \text{concentration of base} \times \text{volume of base}$$

$$\text{concentration of acid} = \frac{\text{concentration of base} \times \text{mL base}}{\text{mL acid}}$$

PROCEDURE

Numbers in parentheses refer to entry numbers on the data sheets.

 I. The sodium hydroxide solution has been standardized. Write its concentration as given on the bottle on the data sheet (1). Obtain about 150 mL of this standard sodium hydroxide solution in a *clean, dry* beaker.

 II. Set up two clean burets as shown in Figure 16-1. Clean each buret until drops of water do not cling to the inside as the buret is drained (Fig. 16-6).

It is neither necessary nor desirable to dry the buret after cleaning.

Figure 15-6. Water drops should not cling to buret.

III. Rinse each buret with two portions of its specific solution in the following manner: Remove the right-hand buret from the assembly and add about 5 mL of the standard sodium hydroxide solution to the buret. A dry funnel may be used or you may pour directly from the beaker. Place your thumb over the open end of the buret and invert the buret several times in order to rinse the inside surface. Under running water, rinse the solution off your fingers. Drain this solution through the tip into a beaker and discard this portion. Finally, fill the buret slightly above the zero mark with sodium hydroxide solution and clamp the buret on the ring stand. Be sure the buret is vertical.

IV. To remove the air bubbles from the tip of the buret, open the stopcock and allow rapid solution flow to flush out air bubbles.

V. With a clean, dry beaker, obtain approximately 150 mL of the unknown acid solution from the instructor. Remove the left-hand buret from the assembly, rinse it twice with 5-mL portions of the acid solution, fill it with acid solution to slightly above the zero mark, remove the air bubbles, and wash any acid off of your hands.

VI. Drain both burets to slightly below the zero mark, then read and record to *two decimal places* the liquid level in each buret (2 and 3). Be careful to follow the reading technique as described in the introduction.

VII. Run out approximately 25 mL of the acid solution into a clean flask. Do not read the exact volume of acid at this time; wait until the titration is completed, because more acid may be required.

Add 4 drops of the phenolphthalein solution to the flask.

Carefully place the flask under the buret containing base and slowly add base, with swirling (Fig. 16-7), until the indicator just changes to the slightest tinge of pink. If too much base is added, add more acid solution until the pink color just disappears. Then add one-half drop of the base, or more if necessary, to restore the slightest tinge of pink. **PATIENCE!**

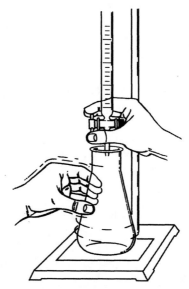

Figure 15-7. Swirl flask during titration.

When a satisfactory endpoint is reached, record the final readings on the burets to two decimal places (4 and 5). Obtain the volumes of acid and base used by difference (6 and 7).

Repeat the titration by refilling the burets with the appropriate solutions. Rinsing is unnecessary the second time.

VII. Calculate the concentration of the acidic solution for each titration (8).

$$\text{conc. of acid} = \frac{\text{conc. of base} \times \text{mL of the base}}{\text{mL of acid}}$$

If the concentrations calculated from these two titrations differ by more than 0.005, a third titration must be performed.

Finally, take the average of the concentrations of acid by adding up all of the concentrations and dividing by the number of titrations performed. Report the average concentration of acid solution to two decimal places (9).

EXAMPLE CALCULATION

Suppose 20.25 mL NaOH is required to neutralize 10.13 mL HCl and the concentration of NaOH is 0.105 M. Find the concentration of HCl:

$$\text{concentration of HCl} = 0.105 \times \frac{20.25}{10.13} = 0.210 \text{ M}$$

PRE-LAB QUESTIONS

1. What would be the effect of placing the standard sodium hydroxide in a beaker which contained some residual water in the beaker?

   _____

   _____

   _____

2. If you were to splash a basic solution into your eyes, what should be your immediate response?

   _____

   _____

   _____

3. If one had one gallon of sodium hydroxide solution which had a concentration of two pounds of sodium hydroxide per gallon, what would be the concentration of four gallons of that acid?

   _____

   _____

   _____

4. Suppose you had 5 gallons of sodium hydroxide solution with a concentration of two pounds of sodium hydroxide per gallon. What is the total amount of sodium hydroxide?

   _____

   _____

   _____

5. What is the purpose of the phenolphthalein solution?

   _____

   _____

   _____

TITRATION OF AN ACID WITH A BASE

(1) Concentration of the standard base   _____ molar

	Run 1	Run 2	Run 3	Run 4
(2) Acid initial reading	_____	_____	_____	_____
(3) Base initial reading	_____	_____	_____	_____
(4) Acid final reading	_____ mL	_____ mL	_____ mL	_____ mL
(5) Base final reading	_____ mL	_____ mL	_____ mL	_____ mL
(6) Total mL used (acid)	_____	_____	_____	_____
(7) Total mL used (base)	_____	_____	_____	_____
(8) Concentration of unknown acid	_____ M	_____ M	_____ M	_____ M
(9) Average concentration of unknown acid				_____ M

Do your calculations in an organized fashion below:

POST-LAB QUESTIONS

1. How do you know when you have added too much standard base (exceeded the endpoint)?

_____

_____

_____

2. Why is it unnecessary to measure precisely 25.00 ml of unknown acid into the beaker?

_____

_____

_____

3. If all the students placed their "unused" standard sodium hydroxide back into the original container what would be the likely effect on the next class?

_____

_____

_____

4. How much 0.150 M sodium hydroxide would be required to just neutralize 15 ml of 0.175 M hydrochloric acid?

_____

_____

_____

Experiment 14

Measurement of pH with Indicators

Performance Goals

27–1   Prepare a set of pH indicator standards.
27–2   Measure the pH of an unknown solution by using indicators.

CHEMICAL OVERVIEW

Solutions of strong electrolytes such as strong acids and strong bases are good conductors of electricity. This indicates a high concentration of ions. In fact, strong acids and bases break into ions almost completely by either of two processes. **Dissociation** is the term used to describe the release of existing ions when an ionic compound dissolves, as in

$$NaOH(s) \rightarrow Na^+(aq) + OH^-(aq) \tag{27.1}$$

Ionization is the process whereby ions are formed when a covalent compound reacts with water, as in

$$HCl(g) + H_2O(\ell) \rightarrow Cl^-(aq) + H_3O^+(aq) \tag{27.2}$$

Even though the terms *ionization* and *dissociation* do not mean exactly the same thing, they are closely related and are often used interchangeably.

By contrast, solutions of weak electrolytes, such as weak acids and weak bases, are poor conductors of electricity. Because current is carried by mobile ions, this indicates a low concentration of ions. We therefore conclude that weak acids and bases are only partially ionized in water solutions. When acetic acid ionizes by reaction with water, equilibrium is reached:

$$CH_3COOH(aq) + H_2O(\ell) \rightleftarrows CH_3COO^-(aq) + H_3O^+(aq) \tag{27.3}$$

At equilibrium, acetic acid is only about 1 percent ionized, compared with HCl, which is nearly 100 percent ionized, as shown by Equation 27.2. Relatively few acetate (CH_3COO^-) and hydronium (H_3O^+) ions are present at equilibrium, but unionized acetic acid molecules (CH_3COOH) are in abundance.

The *acidity* of an aqueous solution is a measure of the concentration of the hydrogen (H^+) or hydronium (H_3O^+) ion.

> **Note:**   The hydronium ion may be considered a hydrated hydrogen ion, $H^+ \cdot H_2O$. The H^+ ion is easier to work with and will be used hereafter. It should be understood, however, that this ion is hydrated in aqueous solution and does not exist as a simple H^+.

A convenient way to express the low acidity of weak acids is to use the **pH** scale. The pH of a solution is mathematically related to the hydrogen ion concentration by the equation

$$pH = -\log[H^+] = \frac{1}{\log[H^+]} \tag{27.4}$$

where [H$^+$] is the concentration of the hydrogen ion in moles per liter. By the mathematics of this equation, pH is the negative of the exponent of 10 that expresses the hydrogen ion concentration. For example, if pH = 5, then [H$^+$] = 10^{-5}; and a solution whose pH = 8 has a hydrogen ion concentration of 10^{-8}, or [H$^+$] = 10^{-8}.

Water ionizes into hydrogen and hydroxide ions:

$$H_2O(\ell) \rightleftarrows H^+(aq) + OH^-(aq) \tag{27.5}$$

At 25°C, the ion product of water—the hydrogen ion concentration multiplied by the hydroxide ion concentration—is equal to 1.0×10^{-14}, or

$$[H^+][OH^-] = 1.0 \times 10^{-14} \tag{27.6}$$

If the ionization of water is the only source of these ions, it follows that they must be equal in concentration:

$$[H^+] = [OH^-] = 1.0 \times 10^{-7} \tag{27.7}$$

A solution in which the hydrogen ion concentration is equal to the hydroxide ion concentration is said to be **neutral.** The pH of a neutral solution is, by calculation, 7. If the hydrogen ion concentration is greater than the hydroxide ion concentration, the solution is said to be **acidic.** In an acidic solution, the pH is less than 7. This is because the negative exponent of 10 decreases as the hydrogen ion concentration increases. [H$^+$] = 10^{-5} (pH = 5) is a larger hydrogen ion concentration than [H$^+$] = 10^{-7} (pH = 7). Conversely, in **basic** solutions, the concentration of the hydroxide ion exceeds the concentration of the hydrogen ion, and the pH will be greater than 7. Note at this point that as the hydrogen ion concentration goes down, the acidity decreases and the pH increases. The pH scale is illustrated in Figure 27–1.

Indicators are organic substances that impart to a solution a color that depends on its pH. Ordinarily, the color will change gradually over a range of about two pH units. In this experiment, you will use two different indicators in a set of solutions of known pH. By comparing colors, you then estimate the pH of an unknown solution.

SAMPLE CALCULATIONS

Example 1

Calculate the pH of a 0.001 M HNO$_3$ solution.
Because nitric acid is a strong acid, we assume that it is completely ionized. Therefore,

$$[H^+] = 0.001, \text{ or } 10^{-3} \text{ mole/L} \qquad pH = 3$$

Example 2

Calculate the pH of a solution that contains 0.01 mole of hydrogen ion in 100 mL.

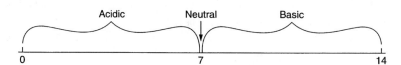

Figure 27–1. pH scale.

First, calculate [H$^+$], always expressed in moles/liter:

$$\frac{0.01 \text{ mole H}^+}{0.100 \text{ L}} = 0.1 \text{ mole H}^+/\text{L} = 10^{-1} \text{ mole/L}$$

It follows that the pH is 1.

Example 3

Calculate the pH of a solution that is obtained when 25.0 mL of 2.0 M HNO$_3$ are diluted to 500 mL.

Remember, nitric acid is assumed to be completely ionized. First, calculate the number of moles of H$^+$ present in 25.0 mL, or 0.0250 liter, of concentrated acid.

$$0.0250 \text{ L} \times \frac{2.0 \text{ moles H}^+}{L} = 0.050 \text{ mole H}^+$$

This many moles of hydrogen ions are present in the final volume, 500 mL. Therefore, the [H$^+$] is

$$[H^+] = \frac{0.050 \text{ mole H}^+}{0.500 \text{ L}} = 0.10 \text{ mole/L} = 1.0 \times 10^{-1} \text{mole/L}$$

The pH of the diluted solution is 1.00.

Alternately, you can carry out a dilution calculation in a single step by multiplying the original concentration by a *dilution factor,* the original volume divided by the final volume:

$$[H^+] = \frac{2.0 \text{ moles H}^+}{L\text{(conc)}} \times \frac{0.0250 \text{ L (conc)}}{0.500 \text{ L (dil)}} = 0.10 \text{ mole H}^+/\text{L (dil)}$$

Original	*Dilution*	*Final*
concentration	*factor*	*concentration*

PROCEDURE

1. WATER PREPARATION

Because carbon dioxide from the air dissolves in water, yielding an acidic solution, we must remove all dissolved carbon dioxide from the water used in this experiment. Place 350 to 400 mL of deionized water in a beaker and heat it to boiling. Continue boiling for approximately 10 minutes, cover the vessel with a large watch glass, and allow it to cool to room temperature.

2. PREPARATION OF STANDARD SOLUTIONS

A.   While the deionized water is being prepared, wash and label six test tubes having a capacity of greater than 10 milliliters. Label them 1 to 6. When the deionized water is at room temperature, prepare a set of solutions as described in Steps B to F. Figure 27–2 is a schematic diagram of the dilution procedure.

B.   As accurately as possible, measure 5.0 mL of 1.0 M HCl into a 50-mL graduated cylinder. Your 5.0-mL measurement will be more accurate if you perform it in a separate 10-mL cylinder and then transfer the solution to the larger cylinder. Dilute the 5.0-mL HCl solution to 50.0 mL, again very accurately, with the treated deionized water. Transfer the contents to a small *dry* beaker and stir thoroughly with a glass rod. Pour 10.0 mL of this solution into test tube number 1.

C.   Carefully and accurately measure 5.0 mL of the solution prepared in Step B into a dry (or deionized-water-rinsed) 50-mL graduated cylinder and again dilute carefully to 50.0 mL with boiled deionized water. Transfer to a clean, *dry* beaker, stir, and pour 10.0 mL into test tube number 2.

D.   Repeat the procedure, using 5.0 mL from Step C, diluting to 50.0 mL. This time, pour 10.0-mL samples into *two* test tubes, number 3 and number 4.

E.   Dilute 5.0 mL of solution from Step D to 50.0 mL in the same fashion and pour 10.0 mL into test tube number 5.

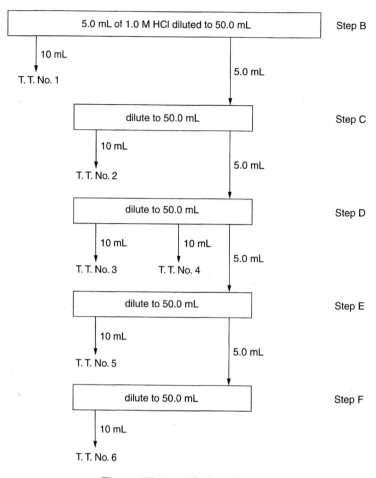

Figure 27–2. Dilution scheme.

F.   Finally, dilute 5.0 mL from Step E to 50.0 mL and pour 10.0 mL into test tube number 6.

G.   If you have not already done so, calculate the hydrogen ion concentration and, assuming complete ionization, the pH of each of the solutions you prepared. Enter the results on the work page.

H.   To each of the test tubes numbered 1 through 3, add 2 drops of thymol blue indicator and mix well with a glass rod. *Be sure the rod is clean and dry before placing it in each solution.* Note the color in each test tube and record your observations on the work page. From these observations, estimate the pH range over which thymol blue changes color.

I.   To test tubes 4 through 6, add 2 drops of methyl orange indicator and mix in the same fashion. Again record the observed color in each test tube, and estimate the pH range over which methyl orange changes color.

Note: If the methyl orange indicator solution is too concentrated, you will see the orange color of the indicator solution itself, regardless of what the pH is. Add only as much indicator solution as is necessary to give a clearly distinguishable color in the various test solutions, or dilute the indicator with deionized water and then add it to the test solutions.

3.   pH OF AN UNKNOWN SOLUTION

Obtain one or more unknowns from your instructor. Pour 10.0 mL of the first unknown into each of two test tubes. To the first test tube, add 2 drops of thymol blue indicator; to the second, add 2 drops of methyl orange (see note above). Mix thoroughly. Compare the colors of these solutions to your "standard" solutions. Basing your conclusions on the colors you observe, estimate and report the pH of the unknown solution. Repeat for each unknown.

Advance Study Assignment

1. If a solution has a pH of 9.5, is it acidic or basic?

2. Calculate the pH of a 0.0001 M HCl solution. If you had an acetic acid solution of the same concentration, would its pH be higher or lower? Explain.

3. Steps 1B to 1F in the Procedure section describe a series of dilutions, beginning with 5.0 mL of 1.0 M HCl. Step 1G asks you to calculate the hydrogen ion concentration and pH for each diluted solution. Perform these calculations now and enter the results in the table below.

Test Tube	$[H^+]$	pH	Test Tube	$[H^+]$	pH
1			4		
2			5		
3			6		

Work Page

Test Tube Number	H⁺ Concentration (mole/L)	pH	Indicator	Color Observed
1				
2				
3				
4				
5				
6				
Unknown No. _____	X X X			
Unknown No. _____	X X X			
Unknown No. _____	X X X			

Estimated pH range of color transition:

    a)   Thymol blue: _____

    b)   Methyl orange: _____

Report Sheet

Test Tube Number	H⁺ Concentration (mole/L)	pH	Indicator	Color Observed
1				
2				
3				
4				
5				
6				
Unknown No. _____	X X X			
Unknown No. _____	X X X			
Unknown No. _____	X X X			

Estimated pH range of color transition:

a) Thymol blue: _____

b) Methyl orange: _____

Experiment **15**

Preparation of Aspirin

Performance Goal

31–1   Beginning with salicylic acid and acetic anhydride, prepare a sample of aspirin.

CHEMICAL OVERVIEW

Chemically speaking, aspirin is an organic ester. An ester is a compound that is formed when an acid reacts with an alcohol (or a compound containing an —OH group):

$$\text{Acid} \qquad\qquad \text{Alcohol} \qquad\qquad \text{Ester} \tag{31.1}$$

where R_1 and R_2 represent alkyl or aryl groups, such as CH_3—, C_2H_5—, or C_6H_5—.

High-molar-mass esters such as aspirin are generally insoluble in water and can be separated from a reaction mixture by crystallization. Aspirin can be prepared by the reaction of salicylic acid with acetic acid:

$$\text{Acetic acid} \qquad\qquad \text{Salicylic acid} \qquad\qquad \text{Aspirin} \tag{31.2}$$

As the double arrow indicates, the reaction does not go to completion, but reaches equilibrium.

A better preparative method—the one you will use in this experiment—employs acetic anhydride instead of acetic acid. Acetic anhydride may be considered as the product of a reaction in which two acetic acid molecules combine, with the resulting elimination of a water molecule:

$$\tag{31.3}$$

The anhydride reacts with salicylic acid to yield the ester (aspirin):

$$CH_3-C\underset{O}{\overset{O\ O}{\diagdown\diagup}}C-CH_3 + 2\ HO-\bigcirc-\overset{OH}{\underset{O=C}{|}} \longrightarrow 2\ CH_3-C\underset{O}{\overset{O\ O=C}{\diagdown}}-\bigcirc-OH + H_2O \qquad (31.4)$$

Acetic anhydride	Salicylic acid	Aspirin
(MM = 102)	*(MM = 138)*	*(MM = 180)*

Excess anhydride reacts with the water produced in the esterification, thereby shifting the equilibrium in the forward direction and giving a better yield of the desired product. A catalyst, normally sulfuric or phosphoric acid, is used to increase the rate of the reaction.

SAFETY PRECAUTIONS AND DISPOSAL METHODS

Both acetic anhydride and phosphoric acid are reactive chemicals that can produce a serious burn on contact with the skin. In case of contact with either, wash the skin thoroughly with soap and water. Avoid breathing acetic anhydride vapors. Wash any spillage from the desk top. The aspirin you will prepare in this experiment is relatively impure and should not be taken internally.

Dispose of any excess solid chemical in a special container. Do not pour acetic anhydride down the drain. Follow the directions given by your instructor.

PROCEDURE

1. PREPARATION OF ASPIRIN

A.   Preweigh a 50-mL Erlenmeyer flask on a decigram balance. Add 1.9 to 2.2 g of salicylic acid and weigh the flask again.

B.   Pour 5.0 to 5.5 mL of acetic anhydride into the flask in such a way as to wash down any crystals of salicylic acid that may have adhered to the walls.

C.   Add 5 drops of concentrated phosphoric acid (85 percent) to serve as a catalyst.

D.   Clamp the flask in a beaker of water supported on a wire gauze (Figure 31–1). Heat the water to about 75°C, stirring the liquid in the flask occasionally with a stirring rod. Maintain this temperature for about 15 minutes, during which time the reaction should be complete.

E.   *Cautiously* add 2 mL of water to the flask to decompose any excess acetic anhydride. Hot acetic acid vapor will evolve as a result of the decomposition.

F.   When the liquid has stopped giving off vapors, remove the flask from the water bath and add 18 to 20 mL of water. Let the flask cool for a few minutes, during which time crystals of aspirin should begin to appear. Put the flask into an ice bath to hasten crystallization and increase the yield of the product. If crystals are slow to appear, it may be helpful to scratch the inside of the flask with a stirring rod.

G.   Weigh a piece of filter paper on a centigram balance before inserting it into the funnel. Collect the aspirin by filtering the cold liquid through a Büchner funnel, using suction, as in Figure 31–2. Disconnect the rubber hose from the filter flask, pour about 5 mL of ice-cold deionized water over the crystals, and suck down the wash water. Repeat the washing step with a second 5-mL rinse of ice-cold water. Draw air through the funnel for a few minutes to help dry the crystals, and then transfer the filter paper and crystals to a clean watch glass.

H.   To determine the yield of aspirin in your experiment, it is necessary that the product be dry. If you do not have time to complete the experiment, store the watch glass carefully in your locker. At the beginning of the next laboratory period, weigh the filter paper and aspirin to the nearest 0.01 g. Record your data in the space provided on the work page.

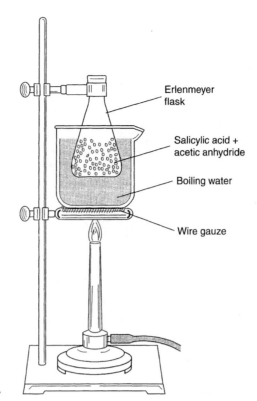

Figure 31–1.
Preparation of aspirin.

2. PURITY OF ASPIRIN (OPTIONAL)

Very pure aspirin melts at 135°C. By determining the melting point of your aspirin, you may estimate its purity, because the purer the aspirin, the closer its melting point will be to 135°C.

A.   Assemble the apparatus shown in Figure 31–3, using a large oil-filled test tube as the heating bath.

B.   Crush some of your aspirin crystals on a watch glass with a spatula. Form a mound from the powder and push the open end of a melting-point capillary into the mound. Hold the capillary vertically and allow it to drop against the table top, compacting the powder into a plug in the bottom of the tube. Repeating the process, build a plug about 3/4 to 1 cm long.

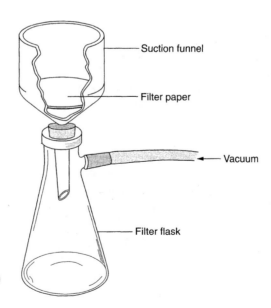

Figure 31–2.   Vacuum
filtration apparatus.

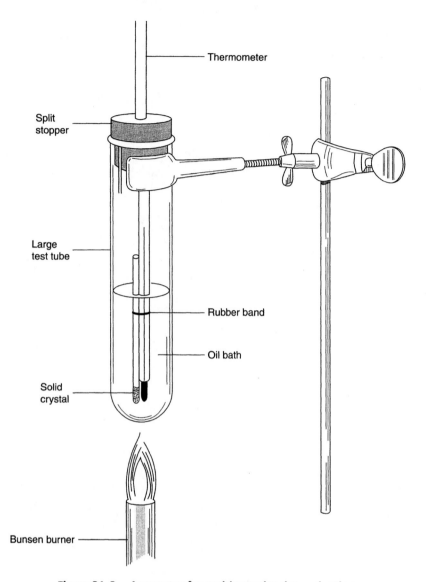

Thermometer

Split
stopper

Large
test tube

Rubber band

Oil bath

Solid
crystal

Bunsen burner

Figure 31–3. Apparatus for melting-point determination.

C.   Attach the filled capillary to a thermometer with a rubber band or slice of rubber tubing, and immerse it in the oil bath. Do not allow the open end of the capillary to come into contact with the oil. Heat the bath rapidly with a Bunsen burner to about 100°C. As the melting point is approached, the crystals will begin to soften. Report the melting point as the temperature at which the last crystals disappear (the tube looks transparent).

CALCULATIONS

The actual mass of aspirin is obtained by taking the mass of filter paper + aspirin and subtracting the mass of the filter paper. Based on the actual mass of salicylic acid used, calculate the theoretical yield of aspirin in grams, using Equation 31.4. Then determine the percentage yield,

$$\text{Percentage yield} = \frac{\text{actual yield}}{\text{theoretical yield}} \times 100$$

where *actual yield* means the number of grams of product actually obtained. Record your results on the work page.

Advance Study Assignment

1. How would you test the purity of aspirin prepared in this experiment?

2. Calculate the theoretical yield of aspirin if you started with 1.75 g of salicylic acid.

3. Identify, by name or formula, R_1 and R_2 in Equation 31.1 when the ester *aspirin* is formed.

Work Page

PART 1—PREPARATION OF ASPIRIN

1A.   Mass of 50-mL Erlenmeyer flask (g)   _____

1B.   Mass of flask and salicylic acid (g)   _____

1C.   Mass of salicylic acid (g)   _____

1D.   Mass of filter paper (g)   _____

1E.   Mass of filter paper and aspirin (g)   _____

1F.   Mass of aspirin (actual yield) (g)   _____

Theoretical yield of aspirin (show calculations below):

_____ g

Percentage yield (show calculations below):

_____ %

PART 2—PURITY OF ASPIRIN (OPTIONAL)

Melting point of aspirin _____ °C

Report Sheet

PART 1—PREPARATION OF ASPIRIN

1A.   Mass of 50-mL Erlenmeyer flask (g)   _____

1B.   Mass of flask and salicylic acid (g)   _____

1C.   Mass of salicylic acid (g)   _____

1D.   Mass of filter paper (g)   _____

1E.   Mass of filter paper and aspirin (g)   _____

1F.   Mass of aspirin (actual yield) (g)   _____

Theoretical yield of aspirin (show calculations below):

_____ g

Percentage yield (show calculations below):

_____ %

PART 2—PURITY OF ASPIRIN (OPTIONAL)

Melting point of aspirin   _____ °C

16 Organic Compounds in Three Dimensions

OBJECTIVE

To become familiar with organic molecules in three dimensions and to understand isomerism of simple organic molecules.

MODELS

Use one of the kits in the lab to make models of organic compounds.

FACTS TO KNOW

Over 11 million of the more than 13 million known compounds are carbon compounds, and a separate branch of chemistry, **organic chemistry,** is devoted to the study of them. Two important reasons why there are so many organic compounds are (1) the ability of thousands of carbon atoms to be linked in sequence with stable carbon–carbon bonds in a single molecule and (2) the occurrence of isomers. The basic geometrics for organic compounds are illustrated below.

Tetrahedron   **Trigonal Planar**   **Linear**

There are four classes of hydrocarbons: **alkanes,** which contain C—C single bonds with a tetrahedral arrangement around each carbon; **alkenes,** which contain one or more C=C double bonds with trigonal planar geometry around the carbon atoms with double bonds; **alkynes,** which contain one or more C ≡ C triple bonds with linear geometry around the carbon atoms with triple bonds; and the **aromatics,** which consist of benzene, benzene derivatives, and fused benzene rings.

Two or more compounds with the same molecular formula but different arrangements of atoms are called **isomers.** Isomers differ in one or more physical or chemical properties such as boiling point, color, solubility, reactivity, and density. Several different types of isomerism are possible for organic compounds. These include structural isomers (straight-chain and branched-chain), *cis* and *trans* isomers, and optical isomers.

The simplest example of structural isomers is for C_4H_{10} which can be either butane or methylpropane.

H H H H

H—C—C—C—C—H

H H H H

butane

H
|
H—C—H
H | H
| | |
H—C—C—C—H
| | |
H H H

methylpropane

In the alkene series, the possibility of locating the double bond between two different carbon atoms add additional structural isomers. Ethene and propene have only one possible location of the double bond. However, the next alkene in the series, butene, has two possible locations for the double bond.

H H H H

H—C=C—C—C—H

H H

1–butene

H H H H

H—C—C=C—C—H

H H

2–butene

An important difference between alkanes and alkenes is the degree of flexibility of the carbon–carbon bonds in the molecules. Rotation around single carbon–carbon bonds in alkanes occurs readily at room temperature, but the carbon–carbon double bond in alkenes is strong enough to prevent free rotation about the bond. This leads to the possibility of *cis-trans* isomers. *Cis-trans* isomerism in alkenes is only possible when both of the double-bond carbon atoms have two different groups.

If two methyl groups replace two hydrogen atoms, one on each carbon atom of ethene ($H_2C=CH_2$), the result is 2-butene, $CH_3CH=CHCH_3$. Experimental evidence confirms the existence of two compounds with the same set of bonds. The difference in the two compounds is in the location in space of the two methyl groups: the **cis** isomer has two methyl groups on the same side in the plane of the double bond and the **trans** isomer has two methyl groups on opposite sides of the double bond. The two arrangements are distinguished from each other by the prefixes *cis* indicating groups on the same side and *trans* indicating groups on opposite sides.

CH_3 CH_3
\   /
C=C
/   \
H   H

cis–2–butene

H CH_3
\   /
C=C
/   \
CH_3 H

trans–2–butene

One class of optical isomers are found for compounds in which four different groups are attached to a given carbon atom as in CHXYZ. As can be seen from the images below, the resultant structures cannot be superimposed on each other no matter how they are turned about:

X X
| |
C⦀⦀Y   Y⦀⦀C
H   H
Z   Z

Mirror

PROCEDURE

In this experiment you will make models of organic compounds using plastic balls to represent the atoms (with different colored balls for different kinds of atoms) and plastic rods to represent the chemical bonds. Using these as a guide, make the models called for and answer the questions. Also consult your textbook for additional information about the different kinds of organic isomers and the rules for naming organic compounds.

PRE-LAB QUESTIONS

1. Why is C_4H_{10} the simplest alkane that can have structural isomers?

   _____

   _____

   _____

2. Draw the *cis* and *trans* isomers for ClCH=CHCl. Why are *cis* and *trans* isomers not possible for $ClCH_2CH_2Cl$?

3. Draw the optical isomers for CHClBrF. Why are optical isomers not found for CH_2ClBr?

Experiment **Name** ______________________

Data Sheet **Date** ______________________

ORGANIC COMPOUNDS IN THREE DIMENSIONS

(1) Make a three-dimensional model of ethane. Are all six hydrogen atoms equivalent? Replace one hydrogen ball by a different colored plastic ball (representing Br). How many isomers of ethyl bromide (bromoethane) are possible? ________________ Draw the structure(s) below.

(2) Make a model of propane. If you substitute one bromine atom for one hydrogen atom, how many isomers are possible? Show what they are and name them.

(3) How many isomers are possible for an alkane with the formula C_5H_{12}? Draw the structures and name them.

(4) Make a model of 1,2-dibromoethene. If *cis–trans* isomers are possible, make models of them. Draw the structures below and name them.

(5) Make a model of 2-methyl-1-butene. How does this differ from 2-methyl-2-butene? Draw their structures.

(6) How many butenes (C_4H_8) are possible? Draw their structures and name them.

(7) Make a model for the molecule CHClBrF. Can the atoms be arranged in more than one way in three dimensions? If so, what is the relationship of the different arrangements? (What is the relationship of your face to the face you look at in the mirror every morning?) Draw structures of any arrange-ments that are different.

(8) Make a model of 2-butyne. Are *cis–trans* isomers possible?

(9) An alcohol is classified according to the kind of carbon atom which bears the −OH group. A carbon atom is classified as primary, secondary, or tertiary according to the number of alkyl groups attached to it. If the carbon atom which bears the −OH group has no or one alkyl group attached to it, the alcohol is a *primary alcohol*. If two alkyl groups are attached, the alcohol is a *secondary* alcohol; if three alkyl groups are attached, the alcohol is a *tertiary* alcohol.

primary alcohol   secondary alcohol   tertiary alcohol

In general, alcohols undergo reactions which are dependent on the type of alcohol used. For example, primary alcohols are oxidized more readily than are secondary alcohols, and tertiary alcohols are oxidized only under severe conditions. Other reactions show similar trends.

Make models of primary, secondary, and tertiary alcohols that have the formula C_4H_9OH. Draw their structures below and name them.

POST-LAB QUESTIONS

1. Why does 2-butene have *cis* and *trans* isomers but 1-butene doesn't?

   _____

   _____

   _____

2. Draw the structural formula of 2-methyl-2-hexene.

3. Which of the following molecules can have optical isomers?

   (a) CH_2Cl_2 (b) $H_2NCH(CH_3)COOH$ (c) $ClCH(OH)CH_2Cl$

Chem 110 Lab Handout   **Experiment 17**

Physical and Chemical Changes;   Law of Conservation of Matter (Mass)

Everything in the universe is composed of matter and energy. Matter occupies space (volume) and has mass (weight). Matter can undergo two basic types of changes: physical and chemical.

Physical Changes:

Physical changes may change the appearance of a substance, but do NOT involve any change in its chemical composition or identity. Some examples are given below

1. A phase change (or change in state): Converting a solid to a liquid and then to a gas involves only a change in the amount of energy in the sample. There is no effect on the chemical identity of the substance. For example, ice, liquid water, and water vapor or steam are all the same substance: H_2O.

2. Crushing a solid into a powder. Or consider the opposite, melting small pellets of plastic and allowing the liquid resolidify into one larger object, such as a cup or a bottle.

3. Some metals (including iron, Fe, and nickel, Ni) can be magnetized. Magnetized iron behaves chemically just like iron that is not magnetic. For instance, both rust easily.

4. Dissolving some crystals of salt in a beaker of water, or the reverse, evaporating the water from a salt water solution leaving behind crystals of salt.

5. Heating some platinum or nichrome wire in a flame until it glows bright red-orange.

Chemical Changes:

A chemical change has occurred whenever a chemical reaction has taken place. After a chemical reaction, new substances will have formed from the original substances that existed before the reaction occurred. Often the new substances do not resemble the old ones in any way. In all cases, the total number of atoms of each kind of element remains the same, but how they are arranged or connected together to form new substances or compounds is distinctly different from their arrangement in the starting materials before the chemical change happened. Signs or observations that often indicate that a chemical change has taken place include:

1. The formation of a gas when liquids or solids are mixed without adding any heat.

2. The formation of a solid (precipitate) when two solutions are mixed.

3. A color change.

4. A change in the acidity or basicity (pH) of a solution.

5. A change in temperature (the evolution or absorption of heat), particularly when flames appear. All chemical changes are accompanied by a change in energy.

For example, paper is made up of giant molecules of cellulose, a compound composed of carbon, hydrogen, and oxygen. If the paper is burned in air (oxygen), a chemical change occurs in which carbon dioxide gas and water vapor are formed. The latter can be condensed to liquid water. Concurrently, much energy is released in the form of light and heat (a flame). A second example of a chemical change is much slower and less dramatic: the silvery metal iron turns to dark orange-brown rust when it is exposed to moist air for a long time.

Law of Conservation of Matter (Mass):

One of the best known and most widely accepted scientific laws is the **Law of Conservation of Matter (Mass)**. It states that during a chemical reaction (change), matter is neither created nor destroyed. An alternative expression of this law declares that the combined total measured mass of all products formed during a chemical change or reaction is equal to the total mass of all the starting materials used up during the reaction.

PROCEDURE

Record all observations and answers to questions in your laboratory notebook. Be sure to measure all masses to three decimal places (that is, to the nearest 0.001 g or nearest 1 *mg*.)

Part I: Physical & Chemical Changes

1A. Record the mass of a clean, dry aluminum, Al, weighing boat. Cut a small piece of wax from a candle and place it into the Al boat. Measure the mass of the boat and the wax. Heat the boat with the wax on a warm hot plate until the wax melts completely. Describe the liquid that forms. Then allow the sample to cool. Again measure the mass of the boat and the wax. Describe the appearance of the wax. What kind of change do each of these transformations represent, physical or chemical? Explain your answers. How much did the total mass change?

1B. Place the Al boat with the wax back onto the warm hot plate until the wax again melts. Carefully take the boat and liquid wax off the hot plate and place it on the lab bench. Immediately stand the candle in the melted wax in the boat. Hold it in a vertical position until the wax cools and resolidifies. Now weigh the candle and the boat. Use a match to light the candle, and let it burn for at least one minute. Record everything you observe. Be sure to sketch the flame and describe its color. After about one minute, extinguish the candle. Record any changes you observe now. Finally, reweigh the candle and the weighing boat. How much did the total mass change? Does this involve physical or chemical changes? Explain.

2A. Tear a small piece of paper (about 5 *cm* × 5 *cm* square) into smaller pieces. What kind of change is involved here?

2B. Put these pieces of paper onto a watch glass and then place the glass on a wire gauze. Ignite (light on fire) the paper with a match and allow it to burn. Record your observations. What kind of change has occurred here?

3A. Add a small spatula full of salt (sodium chloride, NaCl) about the size of a green pea to a test tube containing about 5 *mL* of distilled water. Carefully swirl or stir the contents until all the salt has dissolved. Record your observations. Does this involve physical or chemical changes?

3B. Now use a disposable plastic pipette (dropper) to add approximately ½ *mL* (about 10 drops) of aqueous silver nitrate (0.1 *M* $AgNO_3$) to the test tube with the salt water. What happens? Record your observations. Now swirl or stir the contents of the tube. What do you observe? Gently stand the test tube and its contents in a small beaker or test tube rack. Let it stand undisturbed for several minutes. Have any further changes taken place? Were these chemical or physical changes?   [**CAUTION:** Avoid direct contact with the silver nitrate solution. Silver nitrate can stain your skin or clothing. It is also mildly toxic.]

4.   Obtain a ribbon of magnesium metal [Mg] about 2 *cm* long. Describe its physical properties. Cut this sample into 2 or 3 small pieces. Place these bits of metal into a test tube and use a plastic disposable pipette to add about 2 *mL* of dilute hydrochloric acid [$1.0M$ HCl (aq)]. Record all your observations and state which changes are physical and which are chemical.

CAUTION: Even though such a dilute solution of acid is relatively safe, it could cause chemical burns to your eyes or to sensitive skin, especially about your face. It can also do permanent damage to cotton clothing, ultimately causing holes to form where the acid comes in contact with the fabric.

5A.   Place 5-10 crystals of $CuSO_4 \cdot 5H_2O$ (copper (II) sulfate pentahydrate) into a mortar. Describe their appearance. Now use a pestle to grind these crystals of into a uniform, fine powder. Note any changes you observe. Are these physical or chemical?

5B.   Place a small spatula full of $CuSO_4 \cdot 5H_2O$ crystals into a clean, dry test tube. (The sample should just cover the bottom of the test tube). Use a test tube clamp or holder to gently heat the sample in a small Bunsen burner flame. Be sure to hold the test tube at about a 45° angle and move it constantly in and out of the flame to avoid overheating the sample. Also only heat the bottom part of the test tube. Continue heating gently until the original color of the sample has completely changed. Record your observations. Note also what has occurred near the top of the test tube where it has not been heated by the flame. What kind of changes did you observe?

CAUTION: While heating a sample in a test tube with a Bunsen burner flame, avoid pointing the open end of the test tube at yourself or any other person. Remember hot glass looks no different than cold glass!

5C.   Allow the sample to cool in a test tube rack or small beaker until the test tube is safe to touch. With a pipette place one or two drops of water directly on the sample. What happens? Feel the bottom of the test tube with your fingertip. Record your observations. Is this a chemical or physical change?

Part II: Law of Conservation of Matter (Mass)

1A.   Use a 10. mL graduated cylinder to measure 4.0 *mL* of $1.0M$ NaOH (aq) [sodium hydroxide] solution into a medium-sized (18×150 *mm*) test tube. Then measure 4.0 *mL* of 0.5 *M* $CuSO_4$ (aq) [copper sulfate]. Record the color and appearance of both solutions.

CAUTION: Although a dilute solution of base like NaOH is relatively safe, it could cause chemical burns to your eyes or to sensitive skin, especially about your face. It may also damage clothing, ultimately causing holes to form where the base comes in contact with the fabric.

1B.   Stand the two test tubes with the solutions from **1A** in a 100 *mL* beaker. Now place the beaker with the test tubes and solutions on a balance and measure their combined total mass.

1C. Next pour the NaOH solution into the test tube with the $CuSO_4$ solution. Describe what happens.

1D. Now thoroughly stir the mixture by flicking the test tube with the tip of your finger. [Do **NOT** use a stirring rod.] Let the mixture stand quietly for a minute or so. Describe any additional changes that you observe.

1E. Weigh the 100 *mL* beaker with the two test tubes (the empty one and the one containing the mixture) again to three decimal places. Did the weight change? Why or why not?

2. Repeat steps **1A-1E** again, but this time use 4.0 *mL* of 2.0*M* NH_4OH (*aq*) [ammonium hydroxide] and 4.0 *mL* of 0.5 *M* $CuSO_4$ (*aq*). Measure the total mass as in step **1B** both before and after mixing the two solutions. Again carefully record everything that you observe before and after mixing the two solutions in your notebook.

> **CAUTION:** Although a dilute aqueous solution of NH_4OH is relatively safe, ammonia vapor can irritate the eyes and lungs; the liquid solution may cause chemical burns to your eyes or to sensitive skin, especially around your face. It may also damage clothing and other fabric.

3. Repeat steps **1A-1E** for a third time, but now use 4.0 *mL* of 1.0*M* Na_2CO_3 (*aq*) [sodium carbonate] and 4.0 *mL* of 0.5 *M* $CuSO_4$ (*aq*). Measure the total mass as in step **1B** both before and after mixing the two solutions. Again carefully record everything that you observe before and after mixing the two solutions in your notebook.

4. Repeat steps **1A-1E** for a fourth time. For this last experiment we need two clean beakers. Use the 10 *mL* graduated cylinder and measure 10.0 *mL* of 1.0*M* Na_2CO_3 (*aq*) and pour it into a 50 *mL* beaker; next measure 20.0 *mL* of 1.0*M* HCl (*aq*) into a 100 *mL* beaker. Now measure the total mass of the two beakers and their contents. Next *slowly* mix the two solutions, carefully pouring the Na_2CO_3 (*aq*) into the beaker with the HCL (*aq*). After the reaction is complete, once again measure the total mass of the two beakers and their contents. Make a detailed record of whatever you observe in your notebook before and after mixing the two solutions.

Pre-Lab Questions:

1. A clear, colorless solution of chemical A and a colorless, but cloudy suspension of chemical B had a combined total mass of 1.623 g. After mixing, the new mixture was cloudy and green and had a mass of 1.615 g. Was the Law of Conservation of Mass obeyed during this experiment? What might explain the small change in mass?

2. A clear, colorless solution of chemical D and a clear, red solution of chemical E had a total mass of 1.840 g. After mixing the two solutions, a new orange solution was formed with evolution of many small bubbles of gas. The new solution had a mass of only 1.671 g. What might account for the loss of mass that was observed in this experiment? Was the Law of Conservation of Mass obeyed? Do we have enough information to give a definitive answer the previous question? Please explain.

D. Michael Byler, Chem. Dept., CCP, 20 Sep 2007; revd. 31 Jan 2008